CHRISTIN

UNBROKEN
Rising Above, Thriving Within

UNBROKEN

Rising Above, Thriving Within

CHRISTINE ELLIOTT

Live Free Books

Credits: Edited by Kelsey Connell, Meagan Ong and Gabriel U.
Cover and Interior Design Jennifer Sparks, STOKE Publishing.
Front Cover Photo @juli_labrecque_photography on Instagram.

For bulk purchases or group discounts, please contact Christine at lvfreewellness@gmail.com

Disclaimer: This is not medical advice. This is my personal story. Seek medical advice from a professional.

This book is dedicated to all the people who have supported me throughout my journey - my husband, caregivers, medical team, friends, and family.

I am especially grateful to my four amazing parents, who raised me to be brave and strong, and my four siblings, who have always been there for me.

I also owe a debt of gratitude to my counselor, without whom I wouldn't have been able to learn and integrate the valuable lessons that you will find within these pages.

Thank you.

Contents

Introduction

As we embark on this journey together, I want to express my sincere gratitude to you for choosing to read this book. Your trust means the world to me, and I'm excited to share my story with you.

In the coming pages, I'll share with you my experience with cancer, including the challenges I faced, the lessons I learned, and the transformations that followed. Each chapter is carefully crafted to highlight these lessons and provide you with insights that I hope will inspire and empower you.

In addition to sharing my personal story, I've created a 10-step transformational framework that was instrumental in moving beyond my story, transmuting my experiences, and inspiring change in the face of adversity. This framework, based on the principle of evolution, is designed to help you discover your path to lasting transformation.

The lessons contained within these pages are universal. While my experience with cancer is the backdrop for this book, the insights shared are thoughfully written with the intention of helping people from all walks of life find hope and healing in the face of adversity, challenge, or change.

Before we begin, I want to make a few things clear.

1. This book is not intended to provide medical advice. Always consult with your healthcare provider before making any decisions about your health.
2. While my experience with cancer is a significant theme in this book, the lessons contained within these pages apply to all types of adversity.
3. Finally, I use the term "God" throughout this book, but please know that I welcome and accept whatever term resonates with you.

Thank you again for joining me on this journey. The lessons and insights shared within these pages will inspire and empower you to transform your life and find the peace, joy, and hope you deserve.

PART I
Cancer Cured Me

This is a story about life's lessons, trauma, and overcoming adversity. When trauma hits, we have a choice: to become better or to become bitter. I chose to allow my experiences to teach me. This was the best choice I ever made. Within each chapter, You will find lessons learned highlighted in **bold**. I highlight these lessons in real time in the hopes you may see a reflection in your life through your own challenges. I hope you enjoy and discover moments of reflection, laughter, or enlightenment within its pages. Your experience is a cherished reward for the effort poured into the creation of this book. Your support fuels my passion for storytelling and encourages me to continue sharing my voice with the world.

> **"I can be changed by what happens to me.**
> **But I refuse to be reduced by it."**
> **Maya Angelou**

ONE

The Reckoning

In July 2020, I was blissfully unaware of what was about to transpire in my life. Everything was going smoothly for my husband and I. I worked in a health foods store; I was the fittest I had ever been; I ate well, meditated often, journaled daily gratitudes, and felt at peace in my marriage. We had been married the year prior, and excitedly, we had also decided to have a baby. I was excited about my life, and I felt vibrant and healthy. Yet, unexplainably, I was always tired. This unexplainable exhaustion was beginning to bother me and weigh on my mind. However, I chalked it up to the COVID-19 pandemic. There had been so much stress in the world for months. So, I assumed my exhaustion was a result of that.

That is, until one night, while lying in bed, I noticed a lump in my breast. It was the way that I had looked at my husband, Brad, from across the room that I noticed a considerable divot in my breast. Instinctively, I reached to feel the area. As soon as my fingers touched my skin, my blood ran cold. The tissue underneath my fingers was rock hard like a large gumball had lodged itself inside my chest. I tried to stay calm, but my mind was racing with the worst of thoughts.

I didn't want to worry Brad, but I knew I couldn't keep this to myself. I took a deep breath and called out to him, my voice shaking slightly. When he turned to look at me, I knew he could tell something was wrong. I told him that I had noticed a large breast lump, and his face went white. He, too, felt for the lump and saw that it was alarmingly large. Instantly, my wonderful husband tried to soothe me and exclaimed that it was probably nothing and that we'd deal with it in the morning. He acted casual, but I could see he was worried. I didn't want to push it, and I didn't want to overthink it, so I tried to let it go and attempted to sleep. Sleep did not come.

Instead, I remember staring at the ceiling and crying for hours on end. In my heart, I knew it was breast cancer. The puckered skin, the painful lump, and the fact that it didn't move; It all fit. So now I lay in bed, with tear-stained cheeks picturing what the world would look like without my presence in it. What would it be like for my husband without a wife? My family without a daughter? And my friends without someone to pick up the phone on the other end of their calls? In short, I was devastated.

Staring up at the ceiling, I asked myself, "What did I do wrong?" I was healthy; I ate well, meditated, did yoga, and practiced energy healing. I had been diligently working on my mental and physical health for a decade. I tried to be a good and upstanding person, friend, and daughter. I felt so much shame. I felt like a failure. I had not been doing self-breast exams. After all, I was only 31. I remember thinking of nothing other than absolute dread. My life was about to change whether I wanted to or not.

Late into the early morning, my tears began to subside. Now, I started to get angry. All I could think about was losing the battle and losing my life. The life that was truly beginning. I thought about pain, and I thought about disintegrating into a shell of a human. I thought about chemo and what I pictured a chemo patient to look like. I thought about surgery and losing my breasts. I thought about being burned from radiation. Most of all, I thought about how I had never truly enjoyed my life; **I was always waiting to be happy**, thinner, more successful, and more financially sound to be satisfied. **I put a ton of pressure on myself to be perfect,** and now I wasn't going to get the chance to explore this realization further. What a tragic loss this would be.

Again, I tried to tell myself it could be nothing, but I knew it was breast cancer. No matter how much I didn't want to face it. I thought about our plans, my husband's and mine. We were trying to have a baby, but it hadn't worked. I realized, even then, what a blessing it was that we had been unsuccessful. I remember starting to cry when I thought about the fact that I might never have a baby. Leaving my husband without his dream of being a father and maybe his dream of growing old with me, too. My heart was torn in half with the countless intrusive thoughts that were engulfing me.

The following day, I waited anxiously by the phone until 9:00 AM. When the clock struck nine, I quickly dialed the doctor's office and booked an appointment. The receptionist informed me that the earliest available slot was in a few days. I felt a knot form in my stomach as I realized that I would have to wait for several days before seeing the doctor. Those few days were pure agony; I couldn't stop wondering what was going to happen next. I tried to keep myself busy and distracted, but my mind kept returning to the worst-case scenarios. I felt like I was stuck in a nightmare and couldn't wake up.

Finally, the day came. I went to the doctor's office that afternoon, and the doctor examined me. She appeared unfazed and unconcerned to my delight, which soothed me a bit. However, she said it was best to schedule a mammogram to be sure. Within a week, I was at the screening office. My husband couldn't join me because it was the height of COVID-19, and I was the only one allowed to go to the office. I remember sitting in the waiting room, and something inside me told me this was probably the last typical day of my life.

After completing the mammogram, they asked me if I would be willing to do more tests (not a good sign), and I went on to an ultrasound. I remember sitting in the room looking at a sheet of paper on the wall that said the radiologist would not come in to give me my results because COVID had shut that service down. Then, the radiologist came into the room (yet again, not a good sign). What he said next changed my life forever...

Key Lessons During This Stage of My Journey:

I was always waiting to be happy - *Choosing happiness*

The key lesson is: waiting for an unspecified day in the future to be happy is a waste of valuable time. Life is not always perfect, and hoping for things to improve to attain happiness may never come to fruition from hope alone. Instead, it is important to focus on finding happiness in the present, regardless of any chaos or difficulties that may be present in your life.

I put a ton of pressure on myself to be perfect - *Acceptance*

The lesson to be learned is that perfection is an illusion. Constantly being harsh on yourself is not an effective way to achieve your goals. In fact, it can often have the opposite effect, as it can lead to a downward spiral of negative thoughts and emotions. This results in a lack of motivation and a sense of hopelessness, leading to decreased productivity and decreased progress.

Instead, I invite you to practice self-acceptance and love. This means acknowledging and accepting your flaws and mistakes while recognizing your strengths and accomplishments. By doing so, you create a positive and supportive environment for yourself. Which can lead to increased motivation, productivity, and a sense of overall well-being.

So, the next time you find yourself being too hard on yourself, take a step back and remember that self-acceptance and love will propel you toward your goals much faster than self-loathing and strenuous effort ever will.

TWO

The Flood

"Christine, I have to tell you, our findings are not benign." is what the radiologist started with. Every word he said after these words faded to a murmur. It's like the room went dark, and all I could see was the nurse beside him with a concerned look in her eyes. I noticed his nurse wasn't much older than me. I thanked the staff for their help, I didn't cry, and asked about the next steps. They told me someone would be in touch soon and to try to go home and relax for now. I left the office in a daze and went to my car in the parking lot. Once I reached my car, I noticed a parking ticket on my dashboard. I had forgotten to pay the parking meter amid the chaos and fear of the morning. This was the straw that broke the camel's back. I sat in my car, and I started to cry hysterically.

Upon arriving home, I reluctantly shared the heartbreaking news with my husband. Together, we found ourselves on the edge of our bed, tears streaming down our faces. I vividly recall the moment when Brad's warm eyes turned cold and desolate. In his anguish, he expressed that if he could take the cancer for himself, he would gladly do so. But he couldn't; neither of us could take it away—we were powerless.

Brad wanted to know what actions we would take and what our plan was. However, I couldn't provide him with an answer since I wasn't aware of it at this time. We were instructed to wait, so we had no choice but to be patient and wait.

That afternoon, we decided to continue with our plans for the weekend. I needed something to distract me, so this was the perfect way to take my mind off everything. We had planned to go to the lake where my family was meeting us for a weekend of fun in the sun. I told no one of this unsuspecting news; I couldn't handle talking about it yet. Even my sister, my best friend, didn't know, and I didn't tell her. I simply acted as if nothing had happened. I liked it that way.

We spent the afternoon visiting and making dinner. That evening, we decided to go for a boat ride. Like glass, the lake was perfectly still, and the light breeze was warm and serine. I stared at the water, wondering what would be in store for me, looking around at my family and feeling so guilty that I was about to bring them all so much pain when an unexpected wave of calm washed over me. Suddenly, I felt unbelievably connected to everything around me: the family I was with, the boat's connection to the water, the bird in the sky, the rolling hills in the distance, and the wind in my hair. I don't know that I have ever felt more present in my body than that day.

I don't understand why this experience came to me, but there was an inner knowing that the **experience with cancer was going to change me somehow**. I didn't know how exactly, but something told me that the person I would be on the other side of all this would shake the world. I don't know why I knew it; I did. It was a feeling, an inner knowing. I slept peacefully that night, knowing that, in a way, **I felt more alive than I had ever felt**.

The following days and weeks went by in an absolute blur. I was assigned an oncologist, and in preparation for my appointment, I was thrown into tests upon tests upon tests to get the correct amount of information needed to have an effective appointment. There's so little I remember about that time in my life; I remember needles, scans, nurses, doctors, and counselors on repeat, all with concerned looks in their eyes.

One particularly awful test that I had endured was a biopsy of the tumor. The tumor was located in my left breast at the 9:00 position. Yet again, my husband wasn't allowed to attend the appointment because of COVID-19; He waited outside the hospital anxiously. So, when the surgeon told me that I was going to have to do chemotherapy, Brad wasn't there. When the surgeon told me I might be rendered entirely infertile, Brad wasn't there when the surgeon said to me that I was going to have to get surgery and that I may lose my breasts. Brad wasn't there. When the surgeon told me the cancer may be at a later stage than desired, Brad wasn't there. I remember falling apart and asking the surgeon how much time I had left. With compassion in his eyes, he said that he had faith that we would be able to save my life and that everything was going to be OK. This was the first good news I had received, yet Brad wasn't there.

When our meeting concluded, I was left exhausted and in turmoil. I had received so many extreme pieces of news, yet Brad wasn't there to hear them or to support me. Instead, he was in the truck outside of the hospital. He was not allowed to come inside, and I needed him. I was distraught. There was something inside me that began to shift at that moment. The people pleaser in me wanted to continue obeying the rules set because of COVID-19. However, someone new was starting to emerge. I could feel the fire in my belly begin to burn, and without being able to hold back, I told the nurse that she needed to call my husband at that moment and allow him into the hospital. "The Hell with the rules," I thought. She looked taken aback, but she picked up the phone and told the security guard to let him in. This is the first moment I can recall that **I began to put myself first, unapologetically**.

Brad arrived moments later, and we went into the biopsy together. As the nurse jabbed, cut, and took pieces of the tumor out of my body, I cried uncontrollably. I was thinking about the babies we would never have and thinking about how I felt like a wife who had failed her husband. I felt like I was no longer a woman because I was going to lose my ability to bear children. It was too much, so soon, too fast. The definition of trauma, and there was nothing I could do to stop it.

After the tests were completed, we were pulled back into another room so the surgeon could re-explain everything to my husband. He then understood why I had been crying and began to tear up, too. My treatment plan was said to be about a year and a half long, and I would almost certainly lose my fertility. Brad's dream had always been to have children. I watched his heartbreak in front of my eyes as the doctor said this. He instantly asked if we had options regarding fertility, and to our delight, he recommended IVF embryo preservation. My husband and I shared a glance and then turned back to the doctor. We didn't need to talk about this privately. We both silently agreed this was the best course of action for us and wanted to start immediately. Unfortunately, we were told we had to wait for the biopsy result to go forward everything was a waiting game.

In that same meeting, I challenged the doctor on chemotherapy. I didn't want their poison, and I didn't want to be sick for a year. I wanted to go the healthy route, cut out sugar (which has no detailed research to prove, but I believed it to be confirmed), get surgery, and go back to living life with vitality. With compassion in his eyes, he told me that without chemo, my prognosis was bleak, but with chemo, he was optimistic.

The idea of chemicals was a massive shift in values for me. On the one hand, I had always been a health-minded "health nut." I could remember a time years ago when my stepfather, Rod, decided against chemotherapy, and I was so proud of him for not taking their poison. He went the natural route and did relatively well. His stage 4 lung cancer tumors were shrinking, and he believed in Naturopathic interventions. However, sadly, his condition was too far gone. He ended up with pneumonia, and once that took hold, he passed within days. A hurt that will never fully heal and a hole that will never fully close.

Rod was more than a stepfather to me, I had known him my whole life, and he was loved and cherished as I love my father, he and my mother became a couple when I was only eight years old, and I sorrowfully lost him when I was 25 years old. He was much like a second father, and he was kind and thoughtful and we had so much fun together in the time we shared. When he was diagnosed, my entire family was broken to pieces. With the devastating loss of Rod to cancer, I found myself now facing my diagnosis. The fear and surrealness of it all are indescribable.

When my dear Rod passed away, I admired his conviction so much. The doctors told him that he would undoubtedly die within months, but chemo would give him more time. Rod refused; he would not live out his days sick and frail. He was ridiculed and dismissed for his choice, but he had decided. He lived happily for the next two months, and we spent time together as a family. At that time, I decided that if I were ever faced with the same thing, I would do the same. I would save myself with diet, naturopathic, and positive thinking.

Fast forward to now, and here is a doctor telling me if I take his poison, I'll be ok. But if I didn't, he was unsure of the outcome— the recommendation he was offering made my stomach turn. I went home and planned to contact my naturopathic doctor immediately. I needed her opinion.

In no time, I found myself sitting in the office of a highly quali- fied and compassionate naturopath named Dr. K. She was near my age and had such a light and kind spirit. She listened compassionately as I spoke about my options and affirmed my desire to do things naturally. What she said next shocked me:

"We believe in an integrative approach," she said. She spoke about how, over the years, new literature and research had been published saying that an integrative model is best for cancer. It's a "hit it from all sides" approach. Her explanation of this inte- grative model was music to my ears because I didn't like or trust the medical industry. Still, I certainly trusted the naturopathic sector, and here she was saying I get to, and ought to, do both. I knew this was what I had to do.

I would do the proven medical model and the naturopathic model together. I may not have agreed with both on their own, but together, it appeared palpable. She began telling me what we would do, and I was so intrigued. That is until she told me the prices of these services. My heart sank. It would cost me over one thousand five hundred dollars (plus supplements) a week for five months minimum, and my husband and I had little savings and would soon be losing one of our incomes.

So, back to the drawing board, I went. How would I make money to pay for the medicine I truly believed in? My dear husband, who has always supported me, told me we would find a way, but we both knew that wouldn't be possible. I persevered anyway. I booked my follow-up appointments because I believed in this modality. I had always **lived my life for everyone else and never for myself**. This time, I couldn't do that anymore. This was life or death.

The days continued, and so did the tests. I had yet to find out which way was up and which was down. After a few weeks of what I can only describe as "Hell on Earth," I received a phone call at work one day. The surgeon on the other end of the line let me know that the biopsy results had come back; It was Triple Positive Breast Cancer (so too named by its hormone receptor status). Again, I thought I was ready for this news. I knew it was cancer already, but this poignant diagnosis was so final and so concrete that, again, the room appeared to go dark. The doctor on the phone explained to me that the cancer feeds on three things: estrogen, progesterone, and a protein called Her2. I exited the staff room in a daze and asked to leave for the day. That was the last day I worked in 2020.

Then, a few days later, an MRI scan came back. The tumor, which initially was suspected to be about 3 cm, was a whopping 7 cm with lymph nodes with small tumors in them, and the skin around the tumor had thickened and become inflamed. These findings put my initial staging at a Stage 3C - Stage 3 cancer is exceptionally alarming as the next stage up is Stage 4 - because of this, the doctors told me that I would require additional testing for Stage 4 and I would need to begin chemotherapy right away. You can imagine my shock at all of this information; not only did I have breast cancer, but I might have palliative breast cancer (otherwise known as stage 4 breast cancer).

Two things were true at that moment. One, I needed to get started right away before this grew any further (we had already wasted so much time doing tests), and two, I wasn't going to begin until I had my embryos frozen; **another lesson is choosing myself over people pleasing**. So, contrary to my doctor's wishes, I began fertility preservation the next day.

We took the next step and began IVF fertility preservation. Over the next two weeks, I would visit the fertility clinic and sit in waiting rooms with excited expectant mothers and their partners. I would stare at the wall and try not to cry. Thinking of how they were growing babies, and I was growing cancer every minute of every day that I wasn't in chemotherapy. It didn't seem fair. I remember thinking, "Why me and not them?". It didn't seem fair, right, or. Still, I persevered anyway. I didn't know if I would ever be able to meet these wonderful babies, but I was certainly going to fight hard and try.

The path through IVF was undeniably challenging. Yet, as I type these words for this book, two precious embryos rest, patiently awaiting the arrival of Mom and Dad. Reflecting on this journey fills my heart with an overwhelming sense of completeness. I pray I get to meet these souls one day.

Simultaneously, as I was going through IVF treatments, I felt it was time to tell my family. After all, in a short amount of time, it was nearing the moment for me to begin chemotherapy they would find out soon enough. For nearly a month and a half, I had been fighting this battle alone, and the last thing I wanted to do was cause my family pain but I had to be honest with them as much as myself.

I knew it was time to rip off the band-aid. On a weekend, a few days before my egg retrieval, I was at the lake with my family and began to tell them. I spoke to them individually to protect their privacy (which was much more painful for me in hindsight). They shed tears, and I told them I would be okay - which I didn't know if it was true - and that I wasn't worried - which was all a lie - because I couldn't stand to see them so upset. They were terrified, and so was I. My dad, my hero, who was always so strong, had become quiet and reflective. He looked sick the rest of the weekend, and although I tried to reassure him, he saw right through me. I couldn't stand to see my family so deeply disheartened. I knew it was a normal and natural reaction, but it burned every time. After that, I entrusted my sister to explain to the rest of my family. I couldn't do it. I felt ashamed and disappointed in myself. I had always been such an independent and self-reliant person. However, I simply had hit my breaking point. Breaking my family's and friends' hearts was my breaking point and the brink of my resilience.

I'll never be able to forget what my mother had said when she called me. She said she would be with me every step of the way and was glad we caught it early. I had to tell her it wasn't early. She sobbed. Again, my heart broke..

The mounting pressure kept building up and at this point it had become unbearable. I wasn't sleeping, I wasn't eating, I was rude to my husband, and I wasn't any good to myself or anybody else. It was the lowest of lows, and I hadn't even begun my journey.

To top it all off, well-meaning friends and family began flooding my messages and calls with miracle cures, perspectives, books, and healing modalities. I wasn't complaining, but I was undoubtedly getting confused with all the information. What was the right way to go about my journey? Was I missing something that would make all the difference? I began pouring myself into books and writing lists on lists of "to-do's," I started getting overwhelmed at the thought of all the work ahead of me. I was feeling stretched thin and close to a breakdown.

The moment of the breakdown would come quickly. I will never forget that day. I was on my way to pick up some supplements, covered in bruises and band-aids from the lab appointment earlier that morning, when I received a call from the blood lab. They let me know that the bloodwork that I had performed had clotted and that I had to come back. This was my 17th needle that week. Something broke in me, and I lost it on the technician (which was out of character for me). I slammed the phone and started to scream. I cursed God for what he had done to me; I exclaimed that I didn't deserve this and that it wasn't fair. I screamed, and I hit my steering wheel, and then the tears flowed like waterfalls.

Then, yet another feeling of calm washed over me. I felt held by love, and my tears began to slow. Then, that inner knowing became clear again; something told me this journey would be extremely painful if I stayed in this disparity and anger. I realized then that **I had to practice compassion** for my journey. So, in this moment of clarity. So, in a decision, I metaphorically allow myself to sink to the bottom of a metaphorical pool, knowing I'll understand when I hit bottom and that I'll be able to kick off and resurface with more purpose and power than I have ever had. I don't know what happened that day; perhaps it was my prayers answered. From then on, I became much more aware and intentional about how I felt and **how I was willing to move through my journey**.

Then and there, I resolved **not to subscribe to the victim mindset**. I would not identify as a cancer patient or say things like "F*ck cancer" or that I am a "fighter" or "warrior." These terms may provide inner power for some folks, and that is great if it does. However, I felt it positioned me as a victim of some oppressor. I didn't want to feel weak or outside of my element, so I chose to embrace this experience of cancer. After all, **I grew the cancer. It was part of me and, therefore, part of my life and experience, not separate from it**.

Who did I want to be after all this? What experiences did I want to have? **How could I gain clarity on my goals** as I journeyed? I felt hopeful and at peace. I was going to be ok. I realized that a month and a half had passed, and I had spent that time in a daze. My "Dark night of the soul" had finally hit. I had had my breakdown, and I was ready for what was next and geared up for the upcoming challenges.

What I did when I got home that day was crazy, even to me. I went onto social media, and I told everyone. I told my extended family, friends, followers, and strangers. I did it in a video that blanketed everyone. I spoke about the fact that somehow, inside, I knew I would be ok. I talked about how I knew this would teach me something and that I would make it through and be okay even though I was scared. I don't know why I felt called to share my journey so publicly, but I did, and what followed was such an outpouring of love, kindness, admiration, and thoughtfulness.

I began receiving cards, gifts, and care packages in the mail. I felt floored by people's efforts to show that they loved me. My best friend and cousin discovered I wanted to do naturopathic integrative therapies and started a "Go Fund Me." In a matter of weeks, I went from not knowing how to pay for my treatments to having the exact amount of money that I needed to go forward with the full spectrum of treatments that I wanted to access. My mother, grandmother, and sister made me meals, helped me prepare, and did anything they could within Covid rules and regulations.

To this day, I am in awe of the outpouring of love at a time when we couldn't be close to one another. I didn't realize I meant so much to so many people. **I began to see that I was worth it, that I was loved and had an army of people behind me.**

I began to practice gratitude for everyone in my life, my journey, and the lessons I was learning. Daily, I would write, say, or affirm, "Thank you for my healing." After some time, I began to believe it.

Key Lessons During This Stage of My Journey:

My experience with cancer was going to change me - *Silver linings*

The experiences we go through in life always have the power to change us. Some experiences may be pleasant and joyful, while others may be challenging. However, what's important to remember is that every experience has the potential to teach us something about ourselves and the world around us.

Whether an experience changes us for the better or not is ultimately up to us. We have the power to choose how we respond to each situation we encounter. We can choose to let negative experiences bring us down and hinder our personal growth, or we can choose to view them as opportunities to learn and become stronger.

In the end, it's not the experiences themselves that define us, but rather how we choose to respond to them. So, let's embrace every experience, "good" or "bad," with an open mind and a willingness to learn and grow.

I felt more alive than I have ever felt - *Being present*

One of the most important lessons that life teaches us is the significance of being present in the moment. When you are fully present, you can uplift and center yourself and experience life in its fullest expression. This means that you are not held back by the past or worrying about the future but are fully immersed in the present. Being present enables you to enjoy the little things that make life beautiful and appreciate the people around you. It allows you to connect with your surroundings and find joy in simple pleasures. Practicing mindfulness and becoming present can help you lead a more fulfilling and meaningful life.

I began to put myself first, unapologetically - *Self preservation*

The main takeaway from this lesson is that self-sacrifice often has a backwards effect than intended. When you're constantly sacrificing your own needs to please others, you may be inadvertently create expectations within yourself and among your peers. It becomes a vicious cycle that is hard to break. It's better to be true to yourself and speak your mind, even if it means not always pleasing others. In the long run, self-preservation will lead to healthier relationships and a greater sense of self-worth.

I lived my life for everyone else and never for myself - *Self preservation*

Living for others often creates a disconnect to yourself. From a young age, women are taught to be selfless and put the needs of others before their own. While this may seem like a noble and admirable trait, it often leads to feelings of resentment and a loss of self-awareness. When we consistently prioritize everyone else's needs over our own, we begin to feel that our needs and wants don't matter.

However, putting yourself first can be a healthy and necessary practice. It teaches others how to treat you and permits them to prioritize themselves as well. This can create a more balanced dynamic in which everyone's needs are respected and met.

By prioritizing your own needs, you send a message to others that you value yourself and your time. This can lead to healthier relationships and a greater sense of self-worth. It's important to note that putting yourself first doesn't mean being selfish or neglecting the needs of others. It simply means recognizing that your own needs are as important as anyone else's and making sure they are met healthily and sustainably.

I had to practice compassion - *Compassion*

Life lived without self-compassion can feel unbearable. Often, we set stringent expectations for ourselves, hoping to attain nothing less than perfection. When we fall short of achieving our desired outcomes or find ourselves struggling to navigate our circumstances, we tend to be extremely critical and harsh on ourselves. This self-imposed shame cycle only serves to feed the negativity within us, perpetuating a vicious cycle of self-criticism. Instead of being unkind to ourselves, I invite you to approach your progress with compassion and understanding. By doing so, you will naturally garner results rather than retracting into shame.

I was willing to move through my journey and not subscribe to the victim mindset - Empowerment

The lesson to be learned from this statement is that life is full of choices, and it is up to us to decide what we will choose. We can either choose to see ourselves as victims of our circumstances, or we can choose to empower ourselves and take control of our own lives.

If we choose to see ourselves as victims, we may receive temporary sympathy and love from others, but we will ultimately feel disempowered and helpless with time. In contrast, if we choose to empower ourselves, we may not receive as much pity or attention from others, but we will be able to create a sense of long-lasting happiness and fulfillment in our lives.

To empower ourselves, we must take full responsibility for our actions and decisions and learn to trust our judgment. We must be willing to take risks, make mistakes, and be open to learning from our experiences. By doing so, we can create a sense of purpose and direction in our lives and achieve our goals and dreams.

In summary, the lesson here is that we have the power to choose how we want to approach our journey in life. By empowering ourselves, we can create a sense of happiness and fulfillment that will last a lifetime rather than feeling victimized by circumstances.

I grew the cancer; it was part of me and therefore part of my life and my experience, not separate from it - Trusting your body

Embracing the wisdom of our bodies yields endless benefits. The human body is complex and fascinating. It can both create and heal from illness. When we become sick, it is important to remember that our body is intelligent. Disease is often described as a "Dis-ease" within the body because something is out of balance. The body is not at ease.

In such instances, it is important to remain optimistic and recognize that the body is always trying to heal itself. Our bodies possess an incredible capacity for regeneration and repair, and many illnesses can be overcome with proper care and attention. Often, by simply becoming aware of what our body is trying to tell us.

It is essential to maintain a positive mindset and outlook. Our bodies are energy, and energy can be influenced. Studies have shown that stress and negative emotions can have a detrimental effect on the body and can even suppress the immune system. In contrast, positive emotions and thoughts can help to boost the body's natural healing abilities.

In conclusion, our bodies are truly miraculous and have the power to both create and heal from illness. By taking care of our bodies and maintaining a positive attitude, we can harness this power and overcome even the most challenging health conditions.

How could I gain clarity on my goals? - *Clairity*

Having a crystal-clear goal in mind can be immensely helpful in breaking free from stagnation. When you are clear on your goals, you are less likely to operate on autopilot, which in turn will bring you to your desired result faster. By focusing your energy and attention on your objectives, you begin to make precise and intentional actions that bring you closer to achieving your desired outcome.

I began to see that I was worth it, that I was loved, and that I had an army of people behind me - *Worthiness*

Reshaping our perceptions can have a profound healing effect. Many people spend a significant amount of their lives trying to determine their worth from outside sources. However, some-times, despite their best efforts, they never truly feel valuable. The key to overcoming this feeling is understanding that worth comes from within; it isn't something you earn. It is a decision that you make for yourself rather than something that is bestowed upon you by others.

To feel worthy, there is a shift in your perspective that takes place. Instead of constantly seeking validation from others, you instead focus on recognizing and valuing your unique qualities and strengths. This means accepting yourself for who you are, flaws and all, and viewing yourself as inherently valuable and deserving of love and respect. for existing and being yourself - easier said than done, I know. This is a practice that takes time.

By taking this approach, you can break free from the cycle of self-doubt and self-criticism that can hold you back in life. You can cultivate a sense of self-worth that is based on a deep understanding and appreciation of your worth as a person. This, in turn, allows you live a more fulfilling and meaningful life, one that is characterized by confidence, self-assurance, and a sense of purpose.

I began to practice gratitude - *Gratitude*

Expressing gratitude as a regular practice in your life can have a profound impact on your overall energy and how you approach each day. Even while experiencing pain and difficulty. Taking the time to recognize the things you are grateful for can help you navigate the situation with more ease and tranquillity. By focusing on the positive aspects of your experience, you can shift your energy and mindset in a way that allows you to move forward with greater strength and resilience. Raising your frequency and, therefore raising the quality of your desired results.

THREE

The Chemo

My sister had become an absolute rock star by this point in my journey. My husband had to work away to take care of the loss of finances, so she became the person to bring me to my appointments. At my initial appointment with my oncologist, patients were allowed to bring one loved one to write what the process would entail and what my treatment plan would look like.

Dr. I was a kind and jolly man. The moment he walked through the door, I felt calmer and ready for the next steps. Right away, when he met me, he said, "You are here; you are safe now," something in his sincerity made me believe him. It felt like a match made in heaven; he even believed in integrative medicine as a complementary therapy. Our match felt like a nudge from the universe that I was in the right place. We began discussing my treatment plan, and to say that it was information overload was the understatement of the year. I am so thankful that my sister was there to write notes.

1. The plan was five months of chemotherapy, a surgery of some kind (to be determined), and then 40 days of radiation. Following radiation, a full year of targeted therapy called "Herceptin" would begin (which is a medication designed to cure HER2-positive cancers - this was my particular type of cancer). We would first start with the scans that were necessary to check for stage 4 as we would be beginning chemotherapy one week later, on September 9th. At that point in the meeting, I broke out in a cold sweat. I wasn't ready for chemotherapy, but I knew I had to do it.

A few days later after the needed scans, we began the chemotherapy process with a "port" insertion - which is a tiny mechanism implanted into the arm or chest that acts as a vein for doctors to access injections and blood draws more easily. My veins are unbearably small, and up to this point in my story, I had had to endure one to seven pokes per bloodwork visit; I was covered in bruises, and multiple times, technicians would become frustrated and find a more skilled technician to try again. I was unbelievably exhausted from all of the pokes. I was grateful for this device. The port was inserted into my arm with a local anesthetic, and the following day, I was to begin chemotherapy.

On September 9th my first step into chemotherapy began, my husband took off work, and we arrived early to the chemo ward; he was allowed to come in for the first appointment only. I was in a daze that day and completely unaware of what was happening around me. The chemo ward was lonely, dreary, and hopeless. People around me looked worn down, fearful, and depressed. Most of the nurses looked overworked and tired of the COVID protocols. This ward was not a place I wanted to spend my time. A pharmacy tech and another nurse came to my chairside to explain to Brad and me what to expect. It was over-whelming, and I retained little of what was said. Then, after the initial consultation, Brad was asked to leave for the remainder of my appointment. I was alone for one of the scariest moments of my life. It wasn't fair, and it still makes me angry when I recall the memory.

The nurse assigned to my chair hooked me up using my port and started the machine. First was an antihistamine to help mitigate any reactions I may have, and second was IV steroids designed to increase appetite and reduce nausea, and finally, the chemotherapy itself. I watched the red chemicals (aptly named the "red devil") come down the tube, and I began to pray to God to keep me safe and for this chemotherapy to heal me. I saw it as poison, and I knew that that wasn't going to serve me. So, instead, I prayed. As the red chemicals entered my veins, I began to sob.

After the appointment was complete, I went home and waited. I waited to see how sick I would be. I took a nap, and when I woke up, I was unbelievably nauseous and weak. I spent the rest of the day watching movies and trying to forget about the consistent nausea. The next morning, I woke up and felt a bit better, which was surprising. The day after that, even better. And after four days, I felt fine.

Feeling well so soon was unexpected and exciting! I didn't realize I would get breaks, but I felt good here, and my hair was intact. My morale was high, and I began my naturopathic appointments that week. The regime was simple: twice a week, I would do vitamin C IV therapy; once a week, I would do hyper-thermia therapy. Additionally, I had an entire supplement regime, and my diet was modified to eat as diversely as possible. Finally, I completed mistletoe injections once every few days. Going to these appointments felt exciting and rejuvenating. I believed in this medicine, and I felt that it was what would heal me as the medical system would be what was trying to kill me. However, I knew in my heart that this thought process wouldn't serve me, so I began journaling about it daily. I asked God/universe/source to help me reframe my thoughts on this medicine and help me see it as an opportunity to clean away my body's "slate" so that my naturopathic supports/supplements could then populate my body with health.

Two weeks after the initial chemotherapy, I went in for my second round. I still had my hair and felt good when I went in. After some reflection, I chose to meditate at my appointments. I imagined the chemotherapy was sparkles that were going in and glittering around the tumor, washing the cancer cells away and leaving nothing but health behind. I felt silly with headphones and my eyes closed, but **I chose not to care what people thought**. This was my life, after all.

Previously to cancer, I was a practicing Reiki practitioner, yoga instructor, and self-help enthusiast, and I loved studying energies. **I knew that if I could get my mind on board, raise my frequency, and visualize my healing, my healing would come to me**. So, I continued exclaiming, "Thank you for my healing" nearly daily. I did daily gratitude meditations; I journaled about my gratitude, my lessons, and how I would live once this was over and in the past. I began planning the trips I would go on one day and how I planned to live my "new lease on life." Who did I want to be after cancer? What impact did I want to make in the world? I would ask myself these questions and daydream about the answers. Planning for success became a practice that continued throughout my treatment. Throughout my journey, there were times I was too scared, tired, and worn out to practice, but **I always returned to my beliefs and rituals**. No matter what.

I began to self-advocate and become unapologetic about my needs. I didn't think this would ever be possible. I had spent my entire lifetime living for everyone else and ensuring everyone else was comfortable. Yet here I was doing integrative medicine even though the pharmacy disagreed. I could feel the change within me, and I was loving it.

At about this time, I also began learning and reading about the "Cancer Personality" or "Type C" personality. The theory goes that a particular personality type is prone to certain cancers. This Type C personality has been mentioned in multiple books and medical papers, and although not proven, it is speculated that it could be a contributing factor. My background in energy healing and the study of spirituality aligned with my values and, therefore, became a topic of fascination.

What is the Cancer personality, do you ask? What I have come to observe across all platforms is this: The cancer personality is a person who gives of themselves to everyone except themselves. They are often strong people pleasers and feel isolated and alone in a world of "takers."

I know for myself this described me to a "T," so I began noticing my patterns and decided **it was time to end this cycle of self-deprivation** and enter into a more balanced and peaceful version of myself. My resolve began to inform my decisions and actions as I went through my journey and remains to be a focus today.

That evening, I expected the same level of nausea as the first time; boy, was I wrong! I felt like I had been hit by a truck; I spent most of the evening lying on the cool floor, trying not to vomit. This feeling of nausea, exhaustion, and unwellness lasted much longer than the last infusion. I learned that the medications were cumulative, meaning they built on one another to garner stronger and stronger results (and, therefore, side effects). On top of it all, the steroids that they gave me made it so that I couldn't sleep. I remember staring up at the ceiling, thinking about all the lessons I was beginning to learn, and praying that my life would be spared so I could live these lessons through.

Within days of my second infusion, my hair started falling out. I'll never forget the morning I lifted my head from the pillow, and a handful of hair was left behind on the pillowcase. I felt sick to my stomach at the sight and decided to have a shower to comb the remaining hairs out. I used my fingers to comb out the dead hairs, expecting hairs to cease falling out eventually. They never stopped. I kept combing and combing; clumps of hair kept filling in between my fingers. The sensation of the hairs releasing was uncomfortable and even painful. It felt like a nightmare that I couldn't wake from. I left the shower feeling more nauseous and feeling traumatized. I discarded the handfuls of hair and went into the kitchen, where my grandmother and mother were having coffee.

I was white as a sheet. Concerned, they asked me what was wrong, and I explained what had happened. I knew it was time to shave my head. They agreed, and we got the Clipper. I felt almost excited to take my power back into my own hands. My grandmother was the one to do it, and she giggled and joked the whole way through. We played music, we made it a fun and positive experience. Seeing how much fun she had with the process began to bring me out of my fog, and I began to feel a lot better. Immediately following our buzz cut was a sensation of power and pride. I had taken matters into my own hands and **would not be the victim of my circumstances.** I began to wonder how else I could take my power back. Where else could I practice taking control of my mental state?

The days and weeks following felt like they were on repeat. My sister would take me to my appointments for chemotherapy; then, I would feel awful for days on end and then begin to feel better. Each round was more complex than the last, and each round took longer to come back from the side effects. I began to experience more exhaustion and Weakness, and simple things started to become difficult. I had to **learn how to ask for help** and I had to **learn how to slow down and res**t (two things I was NOT good at). My days were quiet, peaceful, tiring, and sometimes lonely. However, one thing I had was my mind, and that was still strong.

I can remember one day while writing in my journal, I had a realization. I had been writing about how I would like my life to look like one day when this was all over; I wrote things like:

- Wake up with the sunrise without guilt.
- Spend my days helping people and living according to my schedule.
- Eating healthy and vibrant foods.
- Have time to myself to slow down.
- Become compassionate to my own needs and wants.

As I wrote, it dawned on me that I was describing my current day-to-day. Being nauseous, sick, and full of side effects, of course, was not my desire; however, the sentiment remained the same. I was free of rigidity in my work, life, relationships, and inner dialog.

I started channeling the lessons that I was learning into my social media. I used it as a video journal to let my family know how I was doing (since they couldn't see me in person). Talking about my experiences, lessons, and fears was cathartic. I saw it as a way of taking my power back in a place where I could not control anything that was happening around me. As I spoke online repetitively, my confidence began a. to grow.

Simultaneously, I also took my power back with needles. As far back as I can remember, I had been so fearful of needles, and now I had three to twelve needle pokes per week (depending on the integrity of my veins and the skill level of the tech trying to find a usable one). So, I started a ritual to help me get through. I called it a "Poke Card". Every 14 needles (which wasn't hard to get some weeks), I would do something nice for myself. Sometimes, this was as small as a treat/ice cream; other times, it was as large as an entire afternoon of spa treatments. These Poke cards became an impactful source of happiness and resiliency for me.

I began having realizations about my life. I began to see that I had lived my entire life as one huge "to-do" list. I was obsessive about my health, I was obsessive about my weight, I was constantly trying to "fix" myself with self-help books, I needed to be liked by anyone and everyone, and I hadn't **learned how to set a boundary** with anyone in my life. I began realizing I had never **set aside time for intentional rest**; I had always felt so much guilt for relaxation, and I didn't **treat myself compassionately**. These realizations and lessons began pouring in (with the help of my fantastic counselor), and I began to shift as a person.

For the first time in a long time, I started to feel hopeful and excited for the future. I felt that perhaps this cancer was here to transition me into the person that I had always wanted to be. Fearless, self-preserving, unapologetic, and vibrant. I didn't feel well, but inside, I felt better than I had in a long time. That is until I got a call from the doctor.

Key Lessons During This Stage of My Journey:

Chose not to care what people thought - *Embracing you*

One of the most important lessons that we can learn in life is that living solely for the comfort and approval of others can leave us feeling unhappy and unfulfilled. While we may initially believe that shape shifting to become more pleasing to others will bring us happiness and a feeling of belonging, we ultimately discover that this idea is misguided. In fact, it can be incredibly draining to dim our light for others, and it often leads to resentment.

We should never feel ashamed or embarrassed about our quirks or differences, as they are what makes us who we are. By embracing our individuality, we can find a sense of inner peace and happiness that cannot be found by living for others.

So, the next time you feel pressured to conform to someone else's expectations or change who you are to fit in, remember that your uniqueness is God given. Embrace your weirdness and let your true self shine through. You deserve to live a life that makes you happy, and embracing your uniqueness is the first step towards achieving that.

I knew that if I could get my mind on board, Raise my frequency and visualize my healing, then my healing would come to me - *Energetics of healing*

Leaning the concept of frequency in health it is an art all on its own. Energy is fundamental to our existence. Our bodies, minds, and everything surrounding us (including sickness) are made up of energy. The mind-body connection is a well-known phenomenon, and visualization is a powerful tool that can help harness the power of positive energy for physical and mental healing. When we visualize positive health outcomes, we stimulate the brain and nervous system, which in turn can promote the release of hormones that regulate bodily functions.

This can lead to a cascade of beneficial effects on the body, such as reduced inflammation, improved immune system function, and faster healing times. Therefore, by focusing our thoughts and energy on positive outcomes, we promote healing and well-being in both our mind and body.

I always returned to my beliefs and my rituals - *Getting back on track*

One important lesson to keep in mind is that consistency isn't always feasible. It's perfectly normal to occasionally find yourself unable to maintain consistency with your established habits, beliefs, and rituals. Life is full of ups and downs, and sometimes, external factors can make it difficult to adhere to your routines and values. However, instead of beating yourself up or giving up altogether, it's important to approach these situations with compassion and kindness. When you inevitably fall out of integrity, try to identify the reasons why and gently steer yourself back to your established habits, beliefs, and rituals. Remember that progress is not always linear, and it's okay to stumble occasionally as long as you're committed to getting back on track.

I began to self-advocate and become unapologetic about my needs - *Communication*

Life is consistently giving you opportunities to become clear about your needs and desires. Only you can ensure that your needs are met and your voice is heard. By asserting yourself and attracting respect, you will set the tone for how others treat you. Remember, you are in control of your own life, and it's up to you to make sure that you are treated with the dignity and consideration that you deserve.

It was time to end this cycle of self-deprivation. - **C-Type Personality** - **the giver** - *Release the need to give*

The "C-type" personality is the personality of the person who gives too much. leading to stress, burnout and "dis-ease" in the body. People who consistently try to please others often end up giving so much of themselves that they compromise their health and well-being. They tend to put others' needs before their own, leading to physical and emotional breakdown. This leads to a constant feeling of stress and anxiety, which turns on the fight or flight response. This state of being becomes a way of life, and it's not healthy or sustainable.

Additionally, the constant need to be liked and accepted by others can lead to a lack of confidence and self-esteem, which can make it difficult to be assertive, desisive or set boundaries.

To start finding internal self-worth, first, you must recognize you are valuable and worthy of aid and autonomy. This can be achieved by setting boundaries, caring for your own physical and emotional needs, and practicing self-compassion. It may take time and effort, but it's worth it in the end to have a deep sense of self-worth and confidence in yourself.

I was not going to be the victim of my circumstance - *Empowerment*

It is essential to understand that playing the victim will only lead to a sense of powerlessness. Which prevents you from achieving contentment in life. If you constantly see yourself as a victim, your capicity to rise above your circumstances will be diminished. This mindset can be extremely detrimental to your mental health and overall well-being.

Instead of playing the victim, take control of your circumstances and make them work in your favor. By doing this, you will develop a sense of agency, allowing you to take control of your life and steer it in the desired direction. Remember, you are not powerless; your circumstances do not define you. You have the power to shape your life and create a fulfilling and rewarding future.

Therefore, it is crucial to shift your mindset from victimhood to empowerment. Doing this allows you to take control of your life and create a better future for yourself. While the road may be challenging, it is essential to remain optimistic and keep pushing forward. By doing this, you can achieve your goals and live a life that is full of happiness and contentment.

Learn how to ask for help - *Communication*

It's important to remember that the people who care about you are always willing to lend a hand when you are going through a tough time. The most crucial thing is to ask for help when you need it. Trying to handle everything alone and being a martyr won't make you any more valuable or less self-empowered. Embrace the support of others and let them help you.

Set aside time for intentional rest - *Rest*

One of the most valuable lessons I learnt from my experiences is the importance of taking intentional rest. It is a common misconception that working tirelessly without taking breaks will yield better results. The truth is, that overworking yourself only leads to exhaustion and burnout, leaving you with a lack of motivation and decreased productivity in the long run.

Taking intentional rest means giving yourself the time and space to recharge, both physically and mentally. This can take many forms, such as taking a quick power nap, walking, or engaging in a hobby you enjoy. These activities allow your mind and body to relax and rejuvenate, helping you to return to your work with renewed focus and energy.

In the long run, taking intentional rest will help you achieve better results and be more productive. It is a simple yet powerful concept that can significantly impact your life. So, if you feel overwhelmed or burnt out, take a step back and give yourself the gift of intentional rest.

As I wrote, it dawned on me that I was describing my current day-to-day - *Unexpected joy*

The fundamental lesson to learn is that happiness is attainable for everyone if you allow it and embrace it. However, it may not come to you in the way you thought or expected. The path to happiness may require you to take a different approach than desired. At times, the path may look downright awful. It takes persistence and a willingness to keep choosing the happiness you truly desire, over and over again. Then, with time and faith the gifts will be revealed. This means that you must allow the process to unfold without the rigidity of labeling the process as "good" or "bad." The process is what it is.

Learn how to set a boundary - *Boundaries*

Having boundaries is crucial in any relationship, personal or professional. It is important to understand that without clear boundaries, people around you may take advantage of you without even realizing it. However, setting boundaries does not mean you have to be aggressive or confrontational. You can set boundaries with a combination of love and assertiveness. Communicating your boundaries with kindness and compassion demonstrates that you value yourself and your needs. This approach can lead to healthier relationships and a more fulfilling life. Remember to prioritize your well-being and set boundaries when necessary.

FOUR

The Fear

Throughout Chemotherapy, we had been actively performing tests and scans to determine whether I had stage 4 cancer. My bone scan returned negative, my brain scan returned negative, but my lung scan returned <u>inconclusive</u>. When I was told this, the blood immediately drained from my face. I instantly was thrown back into the emotions I felt when I found the lump. Was I going to be OK? Was I going to die? These were questions I didn't know the answer to, and again, I was angry. Angry because I was beginning to get ahead of my initial fears, I was becoming hopeful again, and my stress levels were starting to lower. Then, out of seemingly nowhere, everything had changed yet again.

My oncologist told me that we would watch it and see if it changed in any way. The "nodule" was 2.2 x 1.6 cm and was directly behind my left breast. A worrisome finding as the suspicion was the breast cancer may have spread to the lung. He assured me it could also be nothing, so we had to watch to see If it changed during chemotherapy. If so, we had something to worry about, and if it stayed the same, it was probably nothing, a blip on a scan or a fat deposit. It was easy for him to say, but for me, I had to wait until chemotherapy was complete to see if something changed to determine if I had palliative cancer or curable cancer. I would stare at the ceiling for months and pray. I would cry and scour the internet late at night, trying to figure out what this could be.

I tried my best to keep my mind off it, but it's like trying not to pay attention to the elephant in the middle of the mall; It's impossible. I would watch movies, and as soon as the movie ended, I would remember that I might die - I know that sounds dramatic, but it's what I feared regardless - I began to stare up at the ceiling on my steroid-induced sleepless nights and plan out how I would help my husband transition into my death. I thought about how I would support my family as they said goodbye to their sister, daughter, cousin, and friend. I was thrown back into a depression. I was unsettled, unhappy, and uneasy at every given moment of every given day.

My mind was, once again, consumed with fear and brimming with negativity. I would see people walking by outside my window and ask myself, "Why me and not them?" My prayers, once again, became filled with disdain and anger toward God. Why did he do this to me? What did I do wrong? I was beginning to learn all of these beautiful lessons, and now I was getting the sinking feeling that I was going to lose my life before I would get the chance to live it to my fullest potential.

By this point in my journey, I looked physically ill; my skin was grey, my mouth was full of sores, I had constant nose bleeds, hot flashes, my joints burnt, I had thrush, my fingernails were changing color, I was covered in bruises daily, my face was blotchy, I had no hair, my face was swollen, and I had begun to gain weight (something I did not expect at all). I didn't like the view staring back at me and had started avoiding mirrors. I didn't feel beautiful; I didn't feel feminine. I felt ugly, masculine, fat, and uncomfortable. Not only does cancer leave you fighting for your life, but it also takes away your femininity, your body shape, your libido, your autonomy, and your privacy. I felt angry, lost, confused, and more alone than ever.

Worst of all, my husband had begun to form bags under his already dead-looking eyes. Work had become difficult for him, and he was often distant and alone. He needed support, and I couldn't give it to him. He was terrified; we both were. Neither of us was sleeping.

People around me would try to understand and help me to regain perspective. They would say things like: "My aunt had that, and she lost her battle," or "I once struggled with XYZ, so I think I know how you feel," "Well, at least you got the good cancer," "At least you'll get a free boob job" and (the one I hated the most) "At least it's not Covid, no one can do anything anyways" None of this helped, and that last one enraged me. "Yes, doing this alone without any support, friends, family, helpers, cleaners, drivers, parties in my honor, girlfriends to cry with, food made for me, dinners to keep my mind off things, etc., is excellent... I'm so glad I'm doing this during a pandemic (eye roll)". That is what I would think in my head. To this day, the thought still bothers me. I know these were well-meaning comments, but think before you speak, people!

But I digress; let's get back to the story:

One night, I began to feel physically ill (more than usual), and a fever began to ensue. I checked my blood work online and realized my white blood cells were nearly depleted. Terror filled my mind as I remembered the warnings from nurses and doctors that if a fever is left untreated for too long and the white blood cells are too low, the patient may die. I immediately called my husband and instructed him to come home. He did so, and we rushed to the hospital. Yet again, He wasn't allowed in. I was furious and so angry at this. I needed him by my side, and this was being determined for us. He sat in the truck in the parking lot, not knowing if I would make it. When I entered the hospital emergency, I was greeted by nurses in hazmat suits, sectioned-off waiting areas, and people coughing and hacking. I was terrified. I feared that everyone around me could kill me by giving me COVID-19, yet my reality was that I might not live out the night to find out. I prayed, and I prayed, and I prayed.

The nurses and doctors moved as quickly as possible. The protocol for a cancer patient with a fever is rapid and highly stringent. Within minutes, they tested my blood, put me in a secluded room, started an antibiotic IV, and gave me medications for the fever. Then, there was nothing else to do but wait to see if it improved or worsened. After many hours of fear, hope, and prayers, I began to feel better. I was beside myself with gratitude. Shortly after, the doctor came into the room and told me my fever had broken and that I would be ok after all. They wanted to monitor me to be safe, but I could finally rest. I messaged Brad and my family right away, and the messages of relief I received filled my eyes with tears after a long night, beeps, clipboards, gowns, and pokes. I fell into a peaceful sleep.

With so many extreme experiences happening, I could feel my resiliency waning, and the side effects began to take their toll. After being released I shut myself into my house (which was easy given that the pandemic required us to be home), stopped calling friends and family, and stopped showing up on my social media. After a while, I began receiving calls from friends and family concerned that they hadn't heard from me. I assured them that everything was fine and that I was healing nicely. Which burned every time I lied.

Few people knew how I truly felt, and the few who knew would always say, "If anyone can beat this, Christine, it's you." I clung to these words more than anyone knew.

Regardless of my emotional state, I continued my rituals, journaling, meditating, and affirming that I would be ok. I told myself this was a blip in time designed to bring me to my destiny. Some days, I believed it; other days, I didn't. However, most days, I completed my mental health, energy, and frequency rituals because I believed in them and I believed they would help me.

After months of ups and downs, my active chemotherapy was complete. I still had nine more months of Herceptin treatments. But my hair would begin to regrow, and the worst was over. We had scheduled and completed an MRI to see how the chemotherapy had worked, alongside a CT scan to see if the spot on my lung had changed in any way. Those weeks were tense indeed as I awaited the results of these scans.

Looking back at my chemotherapy now, I can see that among the side effects, the low moments, and the extreme struggles, there were moments of joy. One particular special memory is coming back to my sister's home after appointments and laying on the couch in the sunshine with her new baby tucked into my arms, sleeping and allowing her to take care of me. In these moments, I truly began to heal my obsession with always doing things independently without help. I felt loved and cared for. Those precious moments and that precious baby will forever be an extraordinary memory of mine.

The day my MRI of my breast came back, I was called into my oncologist's office to talk about the results; I was both excited and terrified. I felt hopeful I would be given good news but was at peace knowing I had thrown every healing modality I could at it. When I arrived, he had a huge smile and nearly jumped out of his designer shoes when he told me that I had had almost a "complete result!" Meaning that my 7 cm tumor had shrunk to the size of 1.2 centimeters, my lymph nodes no longer appeared to have any cancer in them, and my skin had healed back to average thickness. We both couldn't believe it; we were elated.

Now, although I do not know what healed me exactly, I am inclined to believe that integrative medicine, combined with my rituals of finding gratitude for the medical model, the prayers said for me, the lessons I was willing to learn, the rituals and visualizations I committed to, my tenacity for life and my conviction that I was going to beat this thing: supercharged the interventions I chose to utilize to combat my cancer. I am not a medical professional, and I don't pretend to know the answer, but I do know that this level of healing was not expected, and yet it happened.

The surgeon and I opted for a 'Breast Conserving Surgery' (otherwise known as a lumpectomy) since the nodule had become so small, and it was my wishful hope to breastfeed someday. I had weighed the pros and cons of a Lumpectomy versus a Mastectomy and was comfortable with the decision.

Which surgery to choose from was a tough decision. So many women choose mastectomies because of the chances of "local recurrence" as well as mitigating scan stress (aptly named "scanxiety"). I researched, and I weighed the pros and cons. Motherhood has always been important to me, and I hope to breastfeed one day. There have been times when I felt shame for not knowing what other Mastectomy survivors go through. There are times I regret my decision (especially when I have abnormal scans or scares), but overall, I am comfortable with my choice. My logic at that time was: "If it returns, I will get a mastectomy. Until then, I will take my chances". To date, it has not returned.

The decision was already made, and the date was set. I went home to tell my husband of the extraordinary news. That was the first bottle of champagne we popped—the first bottle of many.

FIVE

The Interlude

Finally, about a week later, my scan results came in for my CT scan. The nodule on my lung had decreased in size from 2.2 to 1.5cm while going through chemotherapy (not a good sign). I contacted my oncologist to let him know, and we decided to do a lung needle biopsy.

I didn't know exactly how the needle biopsy would go, but my breast biopsy had been painful (due to a local freezing issue), and I had bruising to the point of hemorrhaging from that. So, I wasn't looking forward to what they explained would be a 14-gauge needle entering my back, through my ribs to my left lung. Still, I needed answers, with no choice but to continue anyway.

The morning of the biopsy, I was, again, not allowed to have anyone with me, so I said goodbye to my husband at the door and went inside. Once inside, I was pleasantly surprised and relieved that I knew one of the doctors from my high school days. Having someone in the room that I knew gave me a great deal of comfort; I wasn't alone for once. I put on my gown, took off my jewelry, was given my IV, and was brought into the room. Upon entering the room, I noticed a Bluetooth speaker was playing 90s rap music, Usher, to be exact. I laughed at the comic relief that I should be brought back to even more of my high school years, and I also felt calmer with the distraction my mind conveyed to me too.

The freezing stung, but I couldn't feel anything within minutes. This was a drastic contrast to my breast biopsy, and I felt so much relief. Everything was going well. That is, until my 10-minute biopsy turned into 15 minutes, then 20, then 25, and so on. There was a problem. The problem was the nodule was under a rib, and the needle couldn't reach it. The freezing began to wear off, and the pain started to intensify. I also noticed my breathing was beginning to become shallow (something the doctors nor I expected), and soon after, we had to stop. The pain had elevated, and my breathing was getting shallower by the minute. I was getting apprehensive. It is a human's primary function to breathe, and this loss of breath sent my anxiety through the roof, which only made the pain and shallow breath worse. By the time I was wheeled out, I could barely speak. My breathing was extremely laboured. I was placed under observation and given an x-ray. The doctors were as confused as I was. This wasn't typical.

I was given a relaxant, and the most outstanding nurse sat with me and held my hand. My breathing slowly but surely began to return to normal. She, too, was perplexed at this odd reaction but empathized with how terrifying the experience must have been. She bought me a coffee from the hospital coffee shop and surprised me with it. I don't know her name, but to this day, she remains one of the most admired medical professionals I've ever met. Kindness like that is seldom seen today. Yet, it can make such an impact. I hope she reads this and is rewarded for her kindness and generosity someday.

In discussing my odd encounter with my oncologist later that week, the suspicion was that my lung was spasming due to aggravation. A rare but very real reaction some people have. I felt validated when he told me it can be extremely painful and cause a severe decline in oxygen. Imagine your breath dropping to near-invisible levels. You would be terrified, too, right? This reaction worried me because we still didn't know what would come from my lungs. What if I needed surgery? Would it happen again? These were the thoughts that raced through my mind.

A few weeks passed, and I began to heal from both the biopsy and chemotherapy. I was enjoying the break, and my naturopathic doctor and I started working on rebuilding my immune system. I had gained so much weight from the steroids, and I was feeling ready to get my health back. I felt awful in my body. It felt like salt in a wound to not only have gone through all of the treatments I had gone through but to have also gained weight in such drastic numbers. It was maddening.

We started with rebuilding my protein level intake, including gentle walking into my routine, and added new healing services such as acupuncture, access bars, and massage. Slowly but surely, my taste receptors began to return to normal, my skin rashes and sores began to heal, my hair began to grow, and my skin started to regain colour.

After a few weeks, I got the call. My oncologist told me the results were, unfortunately, Inconclusive. They couldn't get a clear sample due to the complicated location of the nodule. I was gutted. All of that for no reason! "What should we do now?" I asked. He told me the next steps were to do a PET scan (a type of malignancy scan), and we would put a rush on it.

Days later, the scan was booked. The process was overwhelming. A bunch of people in full hazmat suits with full-face face masks put me into a cement room without anything in it. I wasn't allowed to bring anything in, and they injected me with a radioactive fluid that came in a locked and covered machine with warning labels all over it. I was daunted. Afterward, I had to wait for one hour in the empty room while the radiation circulated through my body. They shut the large metal door, and I was locked inside with nothing but my thoughts to keep me company. So, given my condition, as you can expect, this was awful. All I thought about for that hour was: "What the heck is this stuff doing to my body?" "Am I going to be, ok?" "Do I have stage 4 breast cancer?" "Get me outa here!" Finally, the doors opened, and I was escorted to a machine resembling an MRI machine.

The scan was quick, and I was told that it would pick up anything malignancy over 1 cm in size. The precision was good because although chemotherapy had taken the lung nodule down to 1.5 cm, it was still large enough to detect according to those parameters. The scan was completed in minutes, and I was sent home to await the results.

Once again, I waited by the phone for the call. At this point in my journey, I was getting sick of the ups and downs and the waiting game. It was starting to feel like a lashing whip. Never ending. I would begin to get my hopes up, and then shortly after, I would be let down with more bad news. My head felt like it was spinning.

Yet again, my oncologist called. He exclaimed that the scan came back clear! He appeared happy and content with this finding. I should have been elated, but something in me didn't trust it. It was that same sensation as the rush of calm I had experienced months before during the dark night of the soul. Something came over me, a feeling I couldn't shake. I didn't trust the scan and couldn't explain why.

By this point, I had become a strong advocate for my health and couldn't leave this gut feeling alone. So, I asked for another CT scan. I knew it seemed a bit redundant, and it was a big ask, but Dr. I agreed anyway.

Again, we waited.

SIX

The Surgery

While we were waiting for the results of that scan, it was time
for my lumpectomy surgery. I was told that there is a chance I
may lose some breast volume and, therefore, be lopsided. This
news felt like yet another attack on my femininity, and I was
nervous about the result. I am grateful to my husband during
that time because he assured me that I was "beautiful to him no
matter what" daily. Some reassurance I needed during that time.

I was nervous but ready for this part of my chapter to be
complete. Armed with my naturopathic plan, meditations,
husband and family, friends, and social media community
cheering me on, I went in with a whole heart and a readiness for
whatever was about to transpire.

The morning of the surgery had come, and we arrived early. For
the first time in my journey, Brad was allowed in. Having him
by my side changed the experience entirely. I felt safe, comfortable and prepared. The morning was filled with pretests and
procedures, the worst being they had to inject a blue tracer dye
directly into my nipple through a large needle (Yes, it was as
awful as it sounds). Then, they brought me back into the biopsy

room to run a wire to the tumor site. Finally, it was time for surgery. The doctors and nurses were kind, calm, cool and collected. It appeared to them like this was another day at the office. I instantly felt calm and relaxed. Within seconds of the anesthesia, I was out like a light. I woke up in a warm, sunlit room with many nurses around me. I felt pleasantly inebriated, and I felt no pain at all. The drugs were still working. The overall experience was positive, and I was glad of that.

I was wheeled back into my room, where Brad was waiting. He looked delighted to see me, and I felt at ease. We chatted about how I was doing. I said I felt well, but I had one concern; Brad turned to me, looking concerned now. I asked, "Do you think one breast was smaller than the other? (which you couldn't see because of the bandages, but I asked anyway). Brad laughed and told me everything looked symmetrical (he lied), and I felt a sense of relief and contentment wash over me. With the pain managed, I was able to fall asleep and slept for a few peaceful hours. When I awoke, it was time to go home.

I was still sore, and my movement was slower, but overall, I felt ok. I couldn't believe I had been so nervous. Yes, it was painful but bearable. The incision under my arm was much more painful than my breast scar, and I was unable to lift my arms over my head or lift anything for many weeks.

I began physio and started to heal. I couldn't feel any sensation under my arm other than pain and tingling, but I was hopeful it would improve with time. Overall, my experience of breast surgery had been positive.

What I was ultimately more concerned about at this time was my lung CT. As soon as the scan was complete, I logged on to check my results as soon as the scan was complete. To my dismay, the nodule had grown. From 1.5 cm at its smallest, it was now measuring 1.9cm in merely one month without

Chemotherapy. This nodule was increasing, and I wanted to take action immediately. I called my oncologist, who confirmed it was time to talk to a lung surgeon. Within days, I was sitting in Dr. B's office.

We discussed options, and he allowed me to speak about my wishes. I expressed the understanding that my scans were coming back inconclusive or even negative for cancer, but I couldn't take sitting on this for months or even years to "see what it does." He gave me the choice to "opt" for this potentially unnecessary surgery, and I agreed. He told me this wasn't a comfortable surgery, but I didn't care. I wanted this thing gone and was willing to do whatever it took.

The surgery was set for the end of the month, 30 days after my breast surgery. The proximity of the two surgeries daunted me, but I was ready and willing to do what was needed. My intuition was screaming at me to have it removed, and I would not ignore it.

In what seemed like no time at all, I was back in the hospital, ready for round two of surgeries. The morning started on the wrong foot with an argument between Brad and I. It was a dreary day, and the wind was howling. I didn't feel good, and I was nervous. I wanted to call the whole thing off. I knew I couldn't, so we continued. I was terrified my lung would do the same thing it did during the biopsy or worse. What If it spasmed again? What If I lost the ability to breathe easily or even entirely? I couldn't shake the feeling that this would not be an easy surgery. It was hard to cast aside the worrisome thoughts that perturbed my brain.

I finally said goodbye to my husband in the waiting area, and he was told that he could return after the surgery was completed for a short visit in recovery before I had to stay the night in observation. He was told this wouldn't be a lengthy procedure.

I was rolled into the room, and this time, the room was cold, busy, and chaotic. I didn't feel the same comfort level as my last surgery, and I was scared. The gentleman trying to find my IV for my vein missed it multiple times (not an uncommon occurrence), and I was frustrated and exasperated. Then, the anesthesia kicked in, and I fell away.

When I woke up this time, I was not in a sunlit room with kind nurses and a feeling of no pain and inebriation. Unlike before, I woke up with a bright light shining above me with nurses and doctors rushing around with panic in their faces. I could barely breathe, and I was in an immense amount of pain. I couldn't bring in much air at all, and when I did, it hurt like hell. I was fading in and out of consciousness, and it appeared like the lights around me were getting darker and then brighter as the waves of pain thrashed inside my body. I remember a nurse holding me down and begging me to calm down, but I couldn't calm down. I was so panic-stricken I was screaming inside. What is left when you have no air? Nothing. I had nothing left. I had no sense of myself, logic, hope, or clarity. All I had was animalistic panic. The only thought I had in my mind was... I'm going to die.

I do not know how long this lasted as I was in and out of it, but I was informed I was in observation for two hours. It felt like an eternity. To this day, I don't remember much after those moments, the panic and the thrashing of pain. I have tried to search the recesses of my mind while writing this book and have come up with nothing past the moments I've written to you here.

Which must have been hours later, I recall waking up in a dark room with a small dim wall light switched on. My husband was sitting on a chair next to my bed, and he was completely white. His eyes were bloodshot, and he looked physically ill. I asked him what time it was, and he said it was after midnight. He started to tear up as he told me he had no idea what was happening. He had waited until I was supposed to be out of surgery, but no one knew where I was or if I was ok. He told me hours had gone by with no word, and no one would allow him into the hospital as visiting hours were done, so he was not allowed in anymore, and no one would return his calls. Finally, the surgeon called who allowed him into the hospital after hours and let him know where I was. He looked exhausted, and so, so scared. I wanted to reach out to hold him, but my breathing was still shallow, and the pain was severe.

Within minutes, the nurse came in and told Brad he had to go. I began crying and begged her to let him stay longer. I wanted him to hold me and make the pain and fear go away. As he had done so many times before, she agreed, and Brad sat there and held my hand until I fell into a tormented sleep.

Once more, I woke up in pain one hour later. Brad was gone, and the room was dark. I fumbled around for the call button, and a nurse came into my curtained room. I explained that I didn't believe the pain medication was working. She appeared a bit frustrated, but she agreed to give me some over-the-counter pain medication. I was frustrated because that didn't seem like enough. I explained that I was asking for her to provide me with a different pain medication, one that worked, but she refused. She told me only a doctor could order that, and no one could help me. I took the pills, and with mild pain relief, I fell asleep for another hour. This went on all night. I was in pain the entire time. At one point, I had to go to the bathroom, and the nurse explained that I would have to get out of bed to the nearest bedpan. It was embarrassing and painful, and it took two nurses to support me. I remember feeling so low in this moment. I was crying from pain, yes, but most of all, I was crying from a place of depression, sadness, embarrassment, and despair about where I had ended up as this wasn't me or who I ever was.

How did I get here? How is this what God meant for me? I was so angry. Yet again, I asked the question; "Why me? Why me and not them?"

By morning the pain medication was doing absolutely nothing and my body had begun to rash. Once again, I told the nurses I didn't believe the medication was working and this time, I started to get mad. One annoyed nurse finally said to the other "Call the doctor". They didn't speak to me after that.

The doctor came a few hours later, and by this point, I was so angry I was shaking. I didn't care what he thought of me. In the past, I would have been diplomatic and overly polite. I didn't give a damn what he thought about me and I demanded a medication change. He hesitated until I revealed the rash that had developed through much of my body. Then, he finally gave in. Within minutes of the new pain medication entering my veins, the 24-hour pain subsided almost entirely, and I slept blissfully for hours.

When I woke, the pain was nothing more than a dull ache. I reflected on the lessons learned. I had spent my whole life living to impress others. I would sacrifice myself for others' happiness. This time, I was forced to take care of myself. **I vowed to always remember the skill of communicating my needs**.

The surgeon came to talk to me, and we decided together to keep me for a second night due to the severe reaction I had experienced the night before. I was wheeled from the observation ward to a shared room in another part of the hospital. The gentleman in my room was a person with diabetes who had had his leg amputated. My heart broke for him as I heard him moan and groan throughout the evening. The hospital that I was in was old and filled with sad and heavy energy. Throughout the night, I intermittently slept while waking to his groans of pain, feeling intermittent pain myself when the medication would wear off and my incisions would ache. There was a drain connected through my ribs, and whenever I moved, it caused pain.

In the dead of the night, **I began to reflect on my life up to this point**. I had had so much vibrancy and opportunity before this moment. My life has always been so much easier than I had previously thought. like anyone, I had struggles and experiences that hurt me. But physically, I had so much life, vibrancy, and opportunity to be, do, and have anything I had ever wanted.

Now, I was confined to a bed, sharing a room with a man who would never walk again, and I was filled with a humbleness that I had never felt before. In this dark and dreary place, **I vowed never to take another moment for granted again**. The experience of losing my breath taught me that I had taken my ability to breathe for granted. Being confined to this bed taught me that I had taken for granted my ability to walk without pain. Being in this place of such sadness reminded me that I had taken my life and my physical health for granted. I was never going to do that again. I was going to live life in all of its exquisiteness. To truly reflect the blessing of being alive in every single moment of every day going forward. As hard as my experience of lung surgery had been, I wasn't going to squander the lessons that came with it and I was grateful for them.

The following day, I began to feel better. The fluid in my lungs had started to drain, and the nurses and doctors were abuzz, letting me know that soon I would be able to go home. I couldn't wait to get out of this dismal place. I can see now with clarity why patients' health declines rapidly once they enter the hospital. That afternoon, the drain was disconnected, the stitches were put in place, and it was time for me to go home and heal not only in my body but in my mind, too.

Healing from lung surgery while still sore from breast surgery was a grueling process. I could not do simple things and had to rely on my husband for almost everything. Reliance wasn't an easy process, as I had always taken on the role of doing everything. Now, he was left with no choice but to find what we needed in the house to make dinner or clean things. To top it all off, his mental health had begun to decline as well. We were both feeling lost, tired and at the end of our leash.

The lesson of allowing him to take care of me was not a lesson that I expected to have to learn. Yet, it gave me a freedom I had never experienced in my adult life. I had never allowed others to help me. So, this concept was entirely foreign to me. However, I slowly began to improve and **learn to ask for help when I needed it.** Asking for help is not something that most women are conditioned to allow. Most of us are taught to be everything for everybody and never anything to ourselves. Otherwise, we'll be seen as selfish and self-serving. This backward model leaves us tired, lost, resentful, and ineffective. I am not perfect at this, to this day, but this lesson has rippled out into my life in such a beautiful way when I least expected it.

By this point, I began prompting Brad to connect with someone about his mental health. I did not have the capacity or ability to help him and help myself. It broke my heart to watch him in so much pain. He honestly looked sicker than I did. The caregiver goes through so much, yet all support is dedicated to the patient. It is an unfair and broken system. As I disintegrated from five months of chemotherapy and was left traumatized by an awful surgery, Brad was forced to watch helplessly. Men are taught to fix things, and this is certainly something that he simply could not fix. I know now, years later, that what he went through was as traumatic as what I went through with no control over the circumstances. Brad finally sought some support but with the pressures of working and taking on our finances single-handedly. This trauma that he sustained during my journey would come back to haunt us years later.

———————

Key Lessons During This Stage of My Journey:

I vowed to always remember the skill of communicating my needs - *Communication*

The lesson is that when we are clear about our needs and communicate them effectively, people are more likely to help us. Unfortunately, many of us are not taught to be assertive in this way, and we may find ourselves feeling resentful when others fail to intuit our needs and offer assistance.

To avoid this frustration, it is important to cultivate the habit of being clear and assertive. This means being specific about what we need and communicating it clearly and confidently. When we do this, we allow others to assist us in making our lives easier. In practice, this might mean asking for help when we need it, expressing our preferences and opinions clearly, and being willing to find mutually beneficial solutions to problems. By doing so, we can build stronger relationships, reduce stress and frustration, and create a more positive and productive environment in our daily lives.

So, the next time you find yourself struggling to get your needs met on your own, remember that assertiveness and clear communication are powerful tools that can help you get the support and assistance you need. By cultivating these habits, you can transform your interactions with others and create a more fulfilling and satisfying life.

I began to reflect on my life up to this point - *Self reflection*

Taking the time to reflect on your life can be an incredibly powerful tool for gaining clarity and direction. By looking back on your experiences, you can gain a better understanding of where you've been, what you've learned, and how those lessons can inform your future decisions. However, it's important to approach this process with compassion. Rather than judging yourself for past mistakes or missed opportunities, try to view them as opportunities for growth and learning. By doing so, you can move forward with a clearer sense of purpose and a greater appreciation for the journey that has brought you to where you are today.

I vowed to never take a single moment for granted ever again - *Gratitude*

This lesson is often learned due to traumatic experiences. It's easy to get caught up in the busyness of our daily lives, but we must remind ourselves to take a step back and appreciate the little things that make life worth living.

It's a blessing to see the world with new eyes, to gain a fresh perspective, and to realize that the things we once took for granted are often the most precious. This realization is perhaps the most impactful lesson that I learned during my journey. It's a lesson that taught me to live in the present moment, cherish every experience, and be grateful for everything I have.

Life is short, and we must make the most of every moment we have. By embracing this lesson, we can live fulfilled, appreciative, and joyful in this beautiful life.

Learn to ask for help when I needed it - *Communication*

Learning to allow others to help you when you need it can be a challenging task, but it is an essential aspect of self-care. It is not a sign of weakness or laziness but rather an opportunity for you to acknowledge and respect your limits.

Sometimes, we may feel like we need to do everything independently, but that can lead to burnout and exhaustion. By accepting help from others, we can alleviate some of our burdens and focus on what truly matters. Allowing others to help can also be a way of showing yourself grace and love. It shows that you value your time, energy, and overall well-being. It can be a humbling experience to admit that you need assistance, but it can also be empowering. By recognizing that you are worth helping, you are giving yourself permission to prioritize your needs and take care of yourself.

SEVEN

The Radiation

With the surgeries behind me, it was time to think about radiation. I was connected with a radiation oncologist, and the date was set for one month away. After a whole month without treatment, I was ecstatic! It was an entire month of absolutely nothing but healing and relaxing. I spent the month reflecting, journalling, feverishly learning everything I could about cancer prevention, making videos for my social media, and finally decided to start a podcast. I didn't know why I wanted to create a podcast, but I had so much to share about my experiences and needed a platform. I thought, "If I can help one person, it will be worth it." Little did I know that it would turn into helping several from all over the world.

A few weeks into my rest break, I received a call from the lung surgeon. I anxiously answered the phone, nervous about what he would say regarding my pathology. He opened the conversation by questioning my upbringing and my habits. "Did I smoke? The answer was no. Did I grow up around farm chemicals? The answer was not directly. Had I ever heard of radon gas? The answer was no. I began to shake as his questions were concerning."

The surgeon went on to say these words: "You were right; it was cancer." my heart jumped in my chest, and a rush of panic swept over me. He continued, "The crazy part is that this was a primary lung cancer, not stage 4 breast cancer." I felt confused. I asked, "Is that possible?? Two cancers at once??" he replied that it was rare, but it does happen. I was gobsmacked. "Do you mean to say I do not have stage 4 cancer??" I asked. My eyes filled with tears when his answer resounded, "No." The surgeon went on to tell me that the tumor had been removed with clear borders, meaning that the tumor was removed entirely and, therefore, I was now in remission from stage 2B lung cancer.

When I hung up the phone, I sat for a long time staring at the wall, trying to take it all in. "You had primary lung cancer" was not the answer I had expected. I did have cancer, but it wasn't stage 4 cancer; I did not have palliative cancer; I had two curable cancers. I no longer had to fear death or stare up at the ceiling and consider how I would prepare my husband and family for my passing. I couldn't believe my ears. **I was given a second chance—a new lease on life**. I cannot describe in words the joy and relief I had at that moment. The gratitude for this life and the chance to be a part of it. What a blessing it is to be alive!

While telling my family and friends the news that afternoon, a new realization hit me like a ton of bricks:

Without stage 3 breast cancer on the left side of my body, we would have never gone on to test the tumor, fail the tests, and go through with the surgery anyway. I was alive and no longer developing lung cancer because of breast cancer. I was saved from my second cancer because of my first cancer. I had been right all along regarding the sinister nature of the seemly normal nodule on my lung. Something inside of me kept probing me forward to remove it. Even with the best and brightest minds unconvinced. **I listened to my intuition and because of this, I was going to go on living** while so many lung cancer patients did not.

I was here for a reason, and I wasn't going to squander a single moment of this beautiful blessing. My prayers had been answered, and I was going to be okay. I cannot describe that moment any other way other than complete euphoria. That day I touched God's miracle. The miracle was me, in perfect health.

That was the second bottle of Champagne we popped.

The rest of that month was pure bliss. However, it felt like time had sped up, suddenly It was already time for radiation to begin. We decided on a higher radiation dose for nineteen consecutive days instead of forty low-dose days. The radiation's job was to stunt any chance of cancer recurrence, and I was feeling good about this procedure.

The morning of my radiation, I walked down the stairs to the radiation ward rather than up the stairs to the chemo ward, and I remember thinking how cool the "uphill portion" of my battle was over. Even the atmosphere was more hopeful; music played, and nurses laughed and chatted in the hallways. I walked to the radiation room, and a large crew of smiling people greeted me. Inside the room was a large machine that looked like something from a sci-fi movie. A long metal table was in the centre, large enough to fit the patient. I was instructed to undress (which was uncomfortable because we were not allowed to use the changing room because of COVID, and so I had to undress in front of everyone standing there). They covered my lower body in a warm blanket, and the machine began spinning around me. I was a bit concerned that I might feel it or that it might hurt, but it didn't hurt at all. I felt nothing.

My appointment was complete in a matter of minutes, and I was instructed to return the next day. I couldn't believe how easy and painless this procedure had been. After everything I previously had been through, this felt like a walk in the park.

Every day, I would get up and go in for radiation. I would drive myself, and afterward, I would go for a walk or journal or get myself a treat. The process was repetitive but easy, and I was grateful for this stage.

One day, as I was leaving the radiation ward, I received a message on my social media from a patient of the same Cancer Center who had walked by and recognized me from my platform. She messaged me to say she felt like she had a "brush with a celebrity" - I blushed. She said sharing my story gave her hope and impacted her greatly. I thanked her for her enormously generous compliment and reflected on the impact that I had made on her. It was like the heavens opened up, and I realized with clarity that this was what I wanted to do. **I wanted to impact and inspire survivors and women who had a burning desire to evolve past challenges, changes, and shifts in their lives.** This experience would set the stage for what I do now. I will always be grateful to that kind, thoughtful follower who let me know my impact on her.

By day sixteen of radiation, I noticed redness and a general sense of exhaustion. By day nineteen, I was utterly exhausted and ready for a break. In the days following radiation completion, my rash began to blister and bubble, and the skin wilted. I had been warned about this, and although it was uncomfortable, it was nothing compared to the previous months. I could handle a simple rash. I knew what I had to do; I had to set aside time for intentional rest, which is exactly what I did.

Finally, the day came, the day I got the "Ring the bell" I was allowed to bring one person in for my last appointment. My husband was off of his shift at that time, so I finally got to bring him into the hospital and for some good news for a change. At the end of the appointment, I was led to the iconic bell that hung on the wall. This bell symbolizes the end of active treatment and is located in many cancer centers as a beacon of hope for the patients. For me, active treatment was not yet over, but the rigorous portion of my treatment was over, so I couldn't wait to ring the bell to symbolize the completion of a challenging and terrifying year.

I had my husband video the event, and I rang the bell with pride while nurses and patients around me clapped their hands and congratulated me. Ringing the completion bell remains one of my journey's more memorable moments. We spoke about my life going forward. We talked about who I wanted to be and who I wanted to show up as. I told my husband **I would make some BIG changes in how I lived and conducted myself in this world.** I spoke about starting a business helping women evolve, living without apologizing and caring for myself before others. This "alter ego" I would embody would be the best and most exciting part.

I reflected on the lessons I had learned from cancer, and I was moved to tears at all I had learned. I was so excited to get started on my new life. That evening, we popped a bottle of Dom Pérignon with a great friend and celebrated an enormous feat.

Key Lessons During This Stage Of My Journey:

I was given a second chance. A new lease on life - *Live life to the fullest*

Life is a constantly changing journey, full of twists and turns. It is through this journey that we learn the most valuable lessons. One of the most important lessons we can learn from life is that it is always changing, never staying the same or in one place; the world is constantly evolving as we must evolve with it.

However, regardless of how much the world changes, we always have the opportunity to make the most of our time on earth. We have the chance to live fully, appreciate everything we have, and cherish the people in our lives.

It is with the grace of God that we can make the most of our time here. We must always remember that our time on this earth is precious and limited, and we should use it wisely. This lesson has been a gift for me, as it has helped me appreciate the present moment, value the people in my life, and live life to the fullest. This has been such a precious gift for me.

I listened to my intuition and because of this I was going to go on living - *Trusting Intuition*

It is a common occurrence to downplay the power of intuition because of the fear that we may be perceiving things incorrectly or overreacting to situations. However, this distrust we express in ourselves can prevent us from tapping into the intuitive gifts that we are all gifted with. When we ignore our intuition, we are unable to fully benefit from them. We may end up missing out on valuable insights that could have led us to make better decisions.

Have you ever experienced a sense of unexplainable uneasiness about a person or situation, but dismissed it as mere paranoia, only to find out later that your initial instinct was, correct? How many times have you found yourself in turmoil because you failed to trust your intuition? These missed opportunities can have a significant impact on our lives.

Rather than ignore our intuitions, I urge you to listen to them carefully, even if they don't seem to make sense at the time. It may be difficult to trust something that we cannot always explain, but by doing so, we open ourselves up to new possibilities and a more fulfilling life.

I was here for a reason, and I wasn't going to squander a single moment of this beautiful blessing

Need I say more?!

I wanted to impact and inspire survivors and women who had a burning desire to evolve past challenges, changes, and shifts in their lives - *Alchemy*

As you can see, I went on to do that. I am grateful for the cancer that altered my life's direction. I learned that pain can be transformed into power, and I practice this often. I have gone on to speak on stage, write a book, mentor women from all over the world and I live every day with such vigor and joy.

I would make some BIG changes in the way I lived and conducted myself in this world - *Growth*

The experience of trauma can be a difficult and painful one. However, it can also provide us with the opportunity to grow and change. For me, my trauma allowed me to reassess my life and make positive changes. I could break free from old patterns and behaviours that were holding me back and become the person I truly wanted to be. It wasn't easy, but I am grateful for the chance to transform and grow from my experiences. I now see the silver lining in what was once a dark cloud and feel empowered to face whatever challenges come my way.

EIGHT

The After

It seemed anticlimactic that I should have an appointment with my oncologist the following Monday after ringing the bell. Nevertheless, I knew I needed to meet with him to decide our next course of action in my treatment. In the appointment, we decided the following steps were to continue my Herceptin injections for another six months, and I would be assigned five to ten years of anti-hormonal drugs to prevent recurrence. Additionally, on top of that, he let me know there was a new study on a new "post-chemotherapy" drug, and he recommended that I take the drug to reduce my chances of recurrence. I would take this drug for six months intravenously in the chemo ward of the hospital. This chemotherapy would have few side effects, and my hair would stay intact. The wind was instantly taken out of my sails, and the idea of going back into chemotherapy turned my stomach. He assured me that if I could do standard chemo treatments, this therapy would be a breeze. I reluctantly agreed.

I felt frustrated and let down when I left that appointment. I had expected the gruelling portion of my treatment to be over, and yet there was still so much more to go. Worse, days prior, I let my guard down; I was ready for relaxation, not more treatments - so everything following the bell ringing felt like sandpaper to a fresh wound.

I began my anti-hormonal drugs, my monthly medical menopause induction injection into my stomach, the post-chemotherapy infusion, and continued with my Herceptin medications. All of this, all at once, sent me into a tailspin of side effects. As the days and weeks passed, I started feeling more and more desperate for a break. I was angry that there was still so much to do after I'd gone through all the active treatments and surgeries. I began to notice I was getting more and more melancholic, too. I was surprised at this. Remission was supposed to be one of the happiest I had ever been. Instead, I felt tired, worn down, and traumatized. No one understood why I was so frustrated. I didn't understand it myself. Why wasn't I happy? What had gone wrong?

I knew other survivors further along than me had spoken about how survivorship was more complex than active treatment, but I thought they might be acting a bit dramatic or exaggerating. I thought, "That won't be me. I'm not a victim; I'm an optimist". Yet, here I was, sinking lower and lower with each passing moment.

I had constant blood tests, and the appointments were not slowing down. Simultaneously, my side effects that had started to dissipate from active treatment relapsed and came back in full force. I had bone pain, my joints were on fire, I couldn't sleep once again, my hot flashes were off the charts, my skin was dry, my vision was blurred, my libido was gone, and the weight (which had never gone down) was continually piling on.

I was so frustrated I could cry. Here I was, thinking I'd be ready to move on with my life, and I was slapped back into side effects so fast my head was spinning. Wasn't it my turn now? Wasn't it time for me to live well and move on?!

Most of all, I began to feel completely alone. Everyone around me was thrilled that I was "done" treatment. They were expecting the old me to return as quickly as she left, yet she was gone. I didn't know who I was now. I didn't know how to act, what to talk about, or who to spend my time with. I felt dropped in the middle of the ocean on an island with no instruction manual on returning. My support system disappeared all at once. The routine that had propelled me forward every day was gone, and there was no mark to strive or move towards. This mundane life was all it was. No endpoint, no hope.

You see, during active treatment, I was in fight or flight. I ran on adrenalin. After all, death was what awaited me if I stopped fighting. So that felt easier somehow. Now, although things weren't as dire as they had been previously, I had dropped my defenses and relaxed, dropping my walls and exposing all the trauma I had moved through with blinders on. Now, not only was I dealing with the realization of what had transpired, but I was also thrown back into side effects following my medications, I was expected to be "fine" now, but I was not okay and far from it.

I can remember weeks of not being able to get out of bed. I spent all day surfing through my phone, trying to make sense of this "new normal" and how I fit into all of it. I was angry with myself for not being more grateful and ashamed of how sedentary I felt. I stopped posting to social media, went nowhere, and spoke to few people. I was drowning in despair, and I had no idea what to do about it.

I can remember one morning, staring into the mirror looking at my mangled, larger body, and crying for hours. I remember calling a friend that afternoon trying to explain how low I felt to be left misunderstood. "Well, at least your cancer is gone," she said. My heart was utterly broken. She was right, yet I was miserable. I felt completely lost and no one understood.

My husband tried to help me the best he could, but we were in the same boat. We both felt like we had been run over by a truck. At night, we drove aimlessly and lost, driving down the gravel roads, trying to forget. Nothing worked. Months went on like this. I tried to tell my family I was okay, but they saw right through me.

This roller coaster of emotions went on for nearly a year. I would fluctuate from a state of pure bliss for being alive to then crash and burn within hours because of a trigger, whether it was a hot flash, an ache to a pain. The fear of Recurrence filled my mind daily, and I did everything in my power to prevent it. I researched for hours on every internet platform I could find to prevent recurrence. It became my full-time job. I was good at researching and in doing so filled me with a sense of hope. Then simultaneously the anger in me would creep up and I would be reminded that my life would never fully be the same again. It was maddening, to say the least.

Simultaneously, our marriage began silently breaking down. We both had so much sadness and grief that neither one of us could process for the other. We were in a deep financial hole due to a lack of income and Brad's smaller paychecks from working at home (to be close to me). He was quiet and introspective much of the time and I simply didn't have the capacity to help. I was, after all, dealing with my own fears and emotions. Brad wasn't able to let me in and we didn't work as a team, so we began slowly to grow apart without either of us noticing.

You see, the caregivers suffer so much that goes unnoticed. They are left to shoulder the burden with little to no support.

My heart breaks for him when I recall how he must have been feeling. We both feared recurrence so much. It consumed both of our thoughts. I needed to talk about it, and he needed to forget it. However, it was impossible to forget. It invaded every aspect of our lives. Cancer was and is a huge aspect of my life, even still. Whether we liked it or not.

The old adage: "Time heals" is grossly inaccurate. With time, I began to forget and accept my new life, my marriage without romance, my body without health, and my mind without peace. In short, time helped me to settle into my "new normal", but I was far from healed. Still, with time, things began to feel "normal" again. Then, one afternoon, my family received yet another blow.

One afternoon I received a call, that my mother had been diagnosed with breast cancer. I nearly lost my balance. I was floored when I received the news. It was like I was in the twilight zone. After all, I had only just begun to heal myself. I reassured her that everything was going to be ok and that I would be there every step of the way. She was grateful to have me, and I was grateful to be able to provide her comfort. Even still, that night I lay in bed, running through every moment of those first days. Agonizing for her knowing what was in store. Trying desperately to calm my own fears that had been triggered.

I spent as much time as I could supporting her, but the trauma from my past had not yet healed. During each conversation, I felt a burning inside as I remembered her emotions vividly as if they had never left. I became her rock, her guide, and her council. I was honored to take the job. However, I was exhausted. I felt selfish for needing a break, after all. She wasn't getting one. Life went on like this for months. Late night calls, trips to the hospital, and watching helplessly as my mother asked herself the same questions, I had asked myself one year prior.

Her treatment plan was determined after much debate to be surgery, followed by radiation (she had decided against Chemotherapy after seeing what I had gone through). She also decided to go with the naturopathic route as many of my family had done before her. Once the treatment plan was set, there was nothing to do but go through the motions. That is a time I can remember both of us merely surviving.

During this time my husband and I hit a wall; It was time to make a change and we both knew it. We began discussing travel, we had always loved travel. I was hesitant at first as our finances were not that comfortable. However, we both knew if we were waiting for financial comfort, we would never end up going. When it appeared, my mother was out of the woods and on the mend, we then decided together it was time to take a trip. I had always dreamed of Africa, my whole life. When I was diagnosed, I remember thinking about how I never made it to Africa. So, that was the destination we chose. A "Yay you didn't die" trip. We saw and did amazing things. It was the trip of a lifetime! I can recall moments of absolute awe, staring across to African plains, gobsmacked by the thought that there was a time I didn't know If was going to be alive, then, but here I was, staring at a cheetah sunning itself on a rock, or watching the sun set behind an Acacia tree. I could write an entire book about that trip alone. It was the most alive I had ever felt, in a time where everything was still crumbling around me, for once, in a really long time, I was at peace.

In our final days on our dream trip, I can remember counting down the days until I had to return back to my life. Every passing minute felt like agony. The life I had temporarily left at home was not the life I wanted to live. I was unhappy, fearful, working too hard, and giving too much of myself. In Africa I was sovereign. It was as if cancer didn't live in Africa. I didn't have to take my medications (complications with handling and care), my side effects were improving, I was active, and had begun to lose weight. No one asked me how I was feeling or told me about their "aunt who got cancer, and ultimately died". I had nearly stopped thinking about cancer altogether. My mother was on the mend back home and was being taken care of by others who had the emotional capacity to do so. In Africa I had no responsibilities to get back to and nothing but opportunities for adventure in front of me. Most of all in Africa my husband and I had begun to reconnect.

Upon returning home I was flung back into melancholy. Everything I had escaped while away was waiting for me. The medications, the side effects, the doctor's appointments, the responsibilities, the cold, to the empty house with nothing but my thoughts to keep me company. My husband had gone back to work and so I was alone. I decided it was time for a change. Being in utter bliss for six weeks reminded me of the life I wanted to live. I was bound and determined to make a change and I got to work right away. That is until unfortunately, another blow was about to hit me.

A few months after returning, I went in for my yearly scan. The worst had yet again happened - an inconclusive scan. We found out there was a spot of suspicion in my right breast. When I was told this, I was thrown right back into fear. Was my cancer back? Had it returned? Breaking the news to Brad was painful, to say the least. I tried to act casual as the doctors had but he saw right through me. This news sent our marriage into its second (and more deadly) tailspin. Brad became very cold, his eyes appeared all but dead inside, he began hating his work, and worst of all, he stopped talking to me. Within months, I was convinced this was going to be the end of us.

I was angry, not only was I facing a potential recurrence, but I also had the degradation of my marriage to deal with. After many months of anxiously waiting for my second confirmation scan, I was booked for a biopsy of my right breast. The biopsy this time was easy and painless (a good sign), and I was grateful for that. I purchased a bottle of champagne and put it in the fridge, hoping for good news.

A few weeks later, my test results returned. No cancer was detected. Simply an abnormality in the tissues a benign tumour. I let out a huge sigh of relief. Eight months had gone by from the time we found this potential recurrence to when I was given this great news. I popped the champagne, and I told Brad the good news, hoping he would share in my excitement and that I would be able to watch his deadened eyes come back to life. To my dismay, his eyes didn't change. He told me he was happy, but his somber voice said otherwise. Of course, he was pleased, we both were. However, at this point, we had both spent too much time in our stressful and disconnected state. Too much damage had been done. I feared for the worst at this point.

As the time passed, things got worse before they got better. We began fighting, I became resentful and cold. I started picturing what my life would look like without him and I started asking myself if I was naive to believe we could get through this. One afternoon, I finally got up the courage to sit Brad down and tell him about my thoughts and how I felt. I spoke candidly about the fear of our demise and about my leaving. I explained how angry I was to cancer that it had robbed me of so many things, most of all my marriage. He broke down and told me he had never fully dealt with all the trauma he had endured, and I listened with patience, empathy, and understanding. This paradigm-shifting conversation led to the realization for both of us that it was time to return to counseling. To deal with this trauma, three years later.

We found that counselor, an amazingly talented marriage counselor whom Brad had trusted enough to open up to. He began pouring out his feelings and everything he had kept inside. It was like a waterfall. Slowly, but surely, I saw the millions of tons of weight begin to leave his shoulders, his skin brightened, his eyes brightened, and his posture shifted. The burden he had been carrying for all those years had made him weary. His ill health began subsiding and he started to look and act like himself again. It truly was surreal to watch his transformation. I feel privileged to be a part of it. With time, effort, and some big changes in both of our lives, we began to heal our marriage. Today, we have made a full recovery. We are happier and closer than ever before, and I truly feel blessed to have walked this journey with him. In sickness and in health, for richer or for poorer – we have gone through it all.

To finish my story,

This wild ride took four years to move through and although I'm sure the lessons will never be done; I know it is time for the next chapter of my life. I pray I remain cancer-free, but I know our foundation is strong and we can handle anything. My mom has had a full recovery, I no longer deal with side effects, I work out daily, meditate, journal, and count my blessings each and every damn day. It truly is a blessing to be alive and I will never squander that.

I continue to remain good friends with my oncologist, and I volunteer with many organizations and have helped to raise hundreds of thousands of dollars for cancer research; I have spoken on stages at women's empowerment retreats, and I have talked on the radio and on TV to raise awareness about Radon gas and its effects on lung health, I have created courses and support groups and facilitated one-on-one coaching for both men and women from all walks of life in a clinical setting.

Most of all, I am happy. My life has truly begun to become magical. When I was diagnosed, I had an inner knowing that this journey would change me, and it truly has. I have gone after dreams that I would have never had the courage to go after in the past. I have become happy, self-preserving, authentic, and unapologetic about who I am. I have learned to put my needs first and set boundaries around my energy, and most importantly, I do not take a single breath for granted. You could say that **cancer cured me.**

Thank you for reading my story. I hope you have seen yourself in my experiences, no matter what your story is. Ultimately, we are the same, you and I, doing our best with what circumstances we have been given. Thank you for reading, and God bless you in your life. I know no matter what happens to you or has happened to you, it can be turned into your power. That is precisely what the rest of this book is about.

I am thrilled to present to you the latter half of this book. Inside my story, you heard about the lessons I was learning, and now you will read about the concepts in their complete form; you will know how to put these concepts into practice in your own life and turn your adversity and pain into your version of power. I will also offer you an opportunity to dive deeper with me.

I cannot wait for you to transmute and alchemize your own experiences. We can live life unchained and fully expressed. We all go through pain, but I genuinely believe a minority of people truly take that pain and make it into something beautiful. You, my friend, will be one of those people who evolve. Enjoy the following chapters; let us begin.

PART II
Finding Beauty In Adversity

A Step-By-Step Guide to Your Evolution.

I am excited to share with you the following chapters that will help guide you in your evolution. These chapters have been designed to take you from where you are to where you want to be. They have been modeled after my signature transformational programs and thoughtfully crafted with your transformation in mind.

Please note that these chapters have been generalized because I do not currently know your story. So, if anything does not resonate with you, feel free to take what does feel right for you and leave the rest. I also want to clarify that I do not possess all the answers. The insights I share with you are based on my personal experiences and research that I have put into practice. Please keep in mind that these teachings are subjective and should not be taken as absolute truth, but rather as ideas to contemplate.

One of my past clients once told me that working with me felt like I was in the trenches with her, being human and all that comes with it - emotions, messiness, imperfection, and mistakes. My hope for you as you read these chapters is that you can feel my sincerity that you and I are the same, doing the best we can with what we have. I am confident I will have have a few insights that will benefit you.

In these chapters, you will find answers to questions such as who you aspire to become after facing a challenge or adapting to a change in your life, what your secret desires for your future are, and how you wish to be perceived by the world. I truly believe life is not meant to be lived in a routine way, instead, I believe life is meant to be extraordinary. If you have a thirst for more then you have come to the right place.

Thank you for trusting me to guide you through these chapters. I hope you enjoy them.

Christine xo

NINE

Examine

GAINING CLARITY ON OUR DESIRES

The first step in empowerment is to clarify your hidden desires and how you would like to evolve. What is your goal or intention for your future? What experiences have you had that you can utilize to shift you forward? Are you struggling with trauma, divorce, motherhood, low self-worth, disordered eating, career dissatisfaction, neglect in your marriage, etc. (the list goes on)? Then, by being armed with a sense of clarity around our experiences, we can begin to create goals for the transmutation of that experience. Evolution is a process and is the foundation for the rest of the framework.

During my cancer journey, I found that having a clear understanding of my goals and desires was incredibly helpful. This clarity gave me a sense of purpose and direction. When I was feeling overwhelmed or scared, I often reminded myself of my goals and used them as a guiding light to refocus my mind, body, and spirit. I also found it helpful to focus on the things that I could control, like my attitude and my actions, rather than getting bogged down by things that were outside of my control.

By keeping these principles in mind and creating clear goals, I was able to maintain a sense of hope and purpose throughout. While it was undoubtedly a challenging time, these principles helped me to stay strong and focused and ultimately played a role in my recovery and a step toward achieving my goals.

Disclaimer: Growth Is Uncomfortable.

As we embark upon this journey, it is essential to recognize that we will be undergoing a profound transformation that will touch us at the core of our being. The methods and techniques that we have relied on until now may no longer be sufficient to take us to where we need to go. While this realization is crucial, it is also essential to acknowledge that there may be moments of unease along the way as we navigate this new terrain. However, by embracing this discomfort and committing ourselves fully to this process, we can emerge on the other side stronger, wiser, and more resilient than ever before.

What happens when we feel discomfort? We want to move away from it; I get it. This time, we aren't going to do that. This time you will choose you! I like to see discomfort as the "breakdown before the change." It takes love, compassion, patience, and a lot of self-kindness. The good news?? Discomfort always means you are on the verge of a breakthrough!

Facing Our Challenges.

Whether you are a cancer survivor or have experienced any other type of adversity, you *must face it.*

Now, I am not suggesting you go at it alone but with the help of a trusted friend, family member, or counselor you can and must face your story head-on. Otherwise, it will keep gnawing at you. Facing your adversity head-on puts the power back in your hands. By turning away from it, it makes you the victim and the trauma the oppressor.

What happens instead is most of us see the adversity and try our best to avoid or steer clear of it. We tend to put it in a place like the proverbial back burner and numb our pain and distract ourselves with shopping, social media, binge eating, drugs, alcohol, obsessive cleaning, self-controlling environments, etc, etc. This list goes on.

Running from discomfort is a normal and natural reaction to discomfort/adversity. When you burn your finger, you pull your hand away, right? Right. Yet, when we try to numb our pain for too long, we avoid the stove entirely and we are left unfulfilled and malnourished.

The Cycle of Numbing = Shame:

1. We feel pain
2. So we numb,
3. Then, we feel shame,
4. So we beat ourselves up.
5. Then the guilt we feel leads to needing to numb again.
6. The cycle starts anew.

It's no wonder we have a rising epidemic of depression, anxiety, and suicide. The world has become more and more stressful and our capacity to numb has never been more accessible. Self-care has historically been seen as a "luxury-based" skill set. So many people today put self-care at the bottom of the priority list as a result of low energy, willingness, or simply not having enough time.

I know that my initial knee-jerk reaction to my intensified needs was that I was selfish and my needs were unnecessary. I felt ashamed that I was sad, depressed, and unable to conduct myself usually. I also had immense guilt from years of conditioning that if someone is suffering, she simply needs to "pull up her bootstraps and keep working." I know this was wildly unhelpful for me and it wasn't until I learned that it was ok to be sad, it was okay to face my trauma, and ok to rest strategically. That self-preservation is more important than being liked.

This isn't to say there isn't a place for pleasure-based activities. Sometimes numbing is essential. However, the duration of time we spend avoiding our emotions determines the success or failure of aiding or hindering us in life. When we decide to face our challenges head-on with compassion and a curiosity to learn, we can begin to heal our wounds and get back to living the life we desire for ourselves.

Facing your adversity is undoubtedly not a "one and done" procedure. It takes time, patience, and a dedication to repeated efforts. We will be repeating this subject throughout the following chapters.

Getting Crystal Clear on Your Goals Moving Forward.

After taking some time to *identify* the struggles we have gone through, we need to clarify what we *want* moving forward.

So often, we run on autopilot. We have snippets of what we want running through our minds (more energy, healing from sickness, becoming more fit, having a happier marriage, etc.), but we aren't clear on what those things *do* for us. We are often much more transparent about what we DON'T want than what we do want.

An example of this:

- You may feel like you *don't want* to be "depressed" or "sad" because otherwise you feel like a failing parent - *Making you the victim of your circumstance.*
- However, what you actually *want* is to feel vibrant and happy in order to be an active mother/father with your

children. - *Making you the victor in your circumstance.*

Do you see the difference? In the first scenario, you have no "why". There is the avoidance of what you don't want; in the second example, you have a "why" and an end result (in this example, it is "the children "). Reframing your goals this way will lead to a much more effective outcome. When you get *crystal clear on* what you want, then you can start forming a game plan on how to achieve it.

When You Get Crystal Clear, What Happens in The Psyche:

1. First, you **get clear** on your goals and *why. Tip: Start to visualize them.*
2. Then, you **take action** by intentionally making small changes that support that goal.
3. Then, with time, repeated action, and patience, without even realizing it, your **mindset will shift,** leading to more aligned actions.
4. Then, over time your **subconscious**, over time, your subconscious begins to understand what you are looking for and gets on board.

One of the problems we face is that most of us get stuck at talking about our struggles. We are not taught how to move forward. Talking about our challenges is necessary and helpful for the mind. However, there needs to be a point where we move forward and begin to set goals to get ourselves out of our "rut." At this stage, life coaching comes in. As a certified life coach, I help you move forward. So that year after year, you are not facing the same troubles, turmoil, and limiting beliefs holding you back.

What Is the Subconscious Mind?

The conscious mind is responsible for our immediate awareness and perception of our surroundings. It is the part of the mind we use to think, reason, and make decisions. On the other hand, the subconscious mind is the part of the mind that operates in the background and influences our thoughts, feelings, and behaviors without being consciously aware. It is responsible for our automatic responses to certain stimuli and our long-term memory storage. Although we are not usually aware of its workings, the subconscious mind plays a vital role in shaping our overall mental and emotional state. The good news is that time and repetition can influence the subconscious mind. We will be discussing this subject in more detail in future chapters.

A Note from The Author:

We will cover each concept in these chapters quickly but effectively to move you forward from your current state to where you want to be. At the end of the book you will have an opportunity to learn more about my signature group programs to dive deeper into the topics covered here. These programs offer accountability, weekly virtual calls with me, a supportive community, audio, journal questions, meditations, workbooks, and action steps.

The concepts and journal questions in these chapters have the potential to change your experience and create growth on their own. But if you're interested in taking your growth to the next level, you can scan the QR codes in the following graphic and at the end of the book. Any questions you have can be directed to lvfreewellness@gmail.com, and I'd be happy to jump on a free short call to determine your specific needs and create a personalized recommendation for you.

Let's start with your journal questions and action steps to help integrate these principles. Take your time with these:

✅ **Action Step**: Connect with a counselor, professional, friend, or loved one to identify the challenges and changes you want to see in your life.

📖 **Journal Questions**:

- What are your goals for your life? How do you want to feel? What do you want to do? In an ideal world, what opportunities do you want to have? (Have fun with this! Explore! Dream!)
- Next, write beside each goal: *why* do you want those things? What will having those outcomes provide for you?

Enjoy A Free Meditation

Snag Your Complimentary Meditation Session

....

With this book, you'll receive a complimentary meditation designed to assist you in transforming challenges into resilience. This exclusive meditation is specifically for readers of this book. Just scan the QR code provided below to access it.

Free Meditation

This is a meditation that offers support in transforming pain into strength. Embrace the role of the alchemist in your own journey. Use this meditation alongside the book "Unbroken: Rising Above, Thriving Within" for an enhanced experience. Enjoy!

Interested In Learning More About Live Free Wellness?

If you are interested in learning about Live Free Wellness education, 1:1 sessions, public speaking, or free supports, scan the code here to select your preferences. I will reach out via email with the information you requested.

TEN

Realize

UNDERSTANDING OUR STORIES

Understanding and examining the factors holding us back can significantly impact our personal growth. This chapter will identify our limiting beliefs, the narratives hindering our progress, and the self-imposed obstacles. If you feel stuck, this chapter can be beneficial to you. However, be prepared to face some challenging truths.

These concepts have been the biggest motivators for happiness, growth, and positive change. They have the potential to transform your life if you allow them to. I promise you that. During my battle with cancer, understanding these concepts helped me to overcome my fear and depression. They kept me grounded and focused on my goal of healing.

So, let's get started.

Introduction To "Stories" And What "Stories" Do for Us.

Stories are how humans make sense of our environments; they are our mind's way of mapping the world around us.

Our stories are our way of looking at the world. They are constructed from the context of the world we grew up in (i.e., race, gender, financial status, etc.); This is the lens through which we perceive our experiences. The narratives we have are stories that were taught to us by our parents, our teachers, and the community we grew up in. They are the construct of all these things combined.

So how does it work? We tell ourselves a story about our world (through our psychosocial lens of the world).

Examples:

- I am lucky
- I am unlucky
- Life is kind to me
- Life is unkind to me
- My life is abundant
- I can't catch a break

Then, we believe this story because of the context of the world around us:

Examples:

- The job you want becomes available
- You miss the deadline for the job because you are sick
- You get invited to the event you have been dying to go to
- Your friend gets free tickets to the event you wanted to go to
- You find $20 on the sidewalk
- You lose $20 out of your pocket

Then, as a result of our *confirmation bias,* our subconscious mind and the universal laws of the universe (*more on that later) confirms the belief in the story. These roadblocks or easements are often a construct of our own making! I told you this chapter was triggering!

Stories aren't a bad thing. Simply put, the stories we tell ourselves either serve or don't serve us. A few ill-placed stories can lead to a lifetime of havoc. Our stories influence our thoughts which creates the perceptions which then determine our emotions. (clear as mud, right?!)

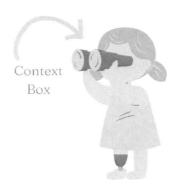

Context
Box

Confirmation Bias Explained.

Confirmation bias is what makes our stories such an influential part of our experience of life. Confirmation bias is a cognitive bias that affects people's perception of reality. It is a tendency to favour information that confirms one's pre-existing beliefs while disregarding or discrediting information that contradicts them. This bias can occur in any area of life and runs in the background without your knowledge of it.

Confirmation bias often happens unconsciously as people tend to seek out information that supports what they already believe to be true. For example, suppose you believe that you could never be a public speaker. In that case, you may seek out evidence that your entire family is uncomfortable with public speaking rather than seeking out evidence that you are a sovereign human and can therefore, accomplish anything with the correct training, mindset, and action taken.

Confirmation bias can also lead people to interpret information in a way that supports their preconceptions. For instance, you may get the courage to speak on stage one day but you will focus on the one person who looks bored and discredit all other interested listeners in the crowd.

The good news? Confirmation bias can become altered simply by getting curious about what your biases are. Gaining clarity on these biases opens the door to choosing new, higher-serving interpretations.

What Are Your Stories?

You may be wondering what your personal stories are. Understanding our stories can be confusing as most of us consider our stories to be facts. Fortunately, there is a simple way to identify your stories; look at your environment! What you experience in your life results from your stories.

For example, if you have a busy and exhausting day-to-day life, your story is likely, "I have to work hard and hustle to have what I want in life." On the other hand, if your day-to-day life is easy and you have plenty of time for relaxation, your story is likely, "The things I want in life come easily to me; life is for enjoying, not grinding."

Neither story is inherently "good" or "bad." These stories simply serve you or don't serve you.

Stories vs. Facts.

Stories can sometimes feel like facts - I get it! The truth is almost all of the stories we tell ourselves are simply stories, not facts. Upon reading this, many will say, "Easy for you to say, you don't have XYZ on your plate," and my reply would be that while that may be true at the moment, it is not a fact that you have to live with. It is a current result of the stories you have been telling yourself about yourself and the world around you.

What's The Difference?

Simply put, stories are impermanent or transient, while facts are permanent. Stories can be changed or altered with a change in mindset, thoughts, and actions; facts are endless, cannot be modified, and are generally past tense.

Examples of Stories vs. Facts:

- **Fact:** You have faced a challenge in your life (cancer, loss, divorce)
- **Story:** Your life will always be difficult due to that challenge.

Stories are subjective; they result from the eye of the beholder. In the example above, the "victim" is the subjective story. The only true fact is that this person had a challenge. Suffering results from how you choose to perceive that situation and its after effects.

The Story Loop:

- You tell yourself a story
- You believe that story to be true

- You find evidence to support that story *by way of the prefrontal cortex (thoughts, actions, and emotions), otherwise known as "confirmation bias"*
- The cycle begins anew.

An Example of The Story Loop:

Let's say you tell yourself the story that life is always difficult for you.

You Say — "Life is always hard for me" — You believe that story to be true

You Believe — "Life is hard because of my awful upbringing" — You notice evidence to support that story

You Confirm — Your mother calls you yelling, your father is neglectful, your sister takes advantage of your kindness — Once you perceive the confirmation the cycle starts anew

Although the example mentioned above may seem true, it is important to note that the storyteller has the power to establish

boundaries with her mother, communicate her needs to her father, and learn to set boundaries with her sister. Stories may appear authentic, but they often stem from a lack of boundaries, self-worth, self-esteem, and a lack of belief in something better.

Why Do We Tell Ourselves Stories?

Humans have an innate ability to create stories; we are inherent storytellers. The stories we choose to tell can either benefit us or cause harm. Stories play a significant role in shaping our world. They help us make sense of things we may not understand or want to deal with. Stories often fulfill a hidden desire or need.

An example of this:

- *Story*: "I am awful at sticking to an exercise schedule."
- *Need/ Subconscious Permission*: This person does not need to hold themselves accountable to the regime.

In the example above, the person telling the story is excusing themselves from having to do regular exercise. The excuse doesn't serve them because they probably wish they were better at exercising regularity.

- *A More Fulfilling Story*: I am committed to exercise and rarely miss a day.
- *New Need/ New Commitment*: This person holds themselves accountable and becomes fit, resulting in a toned and strong body.

Labels Are a Form of Storytelling.

In today's society, we have a tendency to categorize the events that happen to us as either "good" or "bad." However, these labels can lead to unnecessary pain. When something "good" happens, we feel happy, but when something "bad" occurs, we often feel defeated and may even believe that these adverse events; always happen to us.

I want to clarify that I am not dismissing that life can be difficult and unwanted events do not occur. However, I am suggesting that labeling those events as good or bad can prevent us from recognizing the positive outcomes that may come from them. Even in challenging situations, we often overlook blessings when focusing solely on the negative. It is up to us to stay open and receptive to the positives that may arise from any situation.

An Example of This:

You lost your keys and missed the big meeting at work (the label you might place is this was a "bad" morning). However, once you make it to work, you find out that your coworker was tasked with the job you were supposed to do, but since you weren't there, she had to do it (you may label this event as "good" luck)

What it comes right down to is that in the above example, neither label is accurate. It is what it is. These are simply events; some feel good, while others feel bad: it is all about perception. The only reason these things feel this way is because of our labels and expectations.

The Role of Our Expectations.

We tend to set expectations for ourselves as well as others around us. These expectations are based on our beliefs, values, and experiences. It can be pretty disappointing when we expect a specific outcome that doesn't come to fruition. We feel pain and discomfort when our expectations are not met. This pain is often a result of the gap between what we expected and what happened.

Expectations can be a significant source of suffering. We often create expectations to control our environment and avoid pain. We believe that if we can manage our expectations we can prevent pain and disappointment. However, the paradox is that expectations often do the opposite. When we set expectations, we create a rigid framework that limits our ability to adapt to changing circumstances; this can lead to frustration, anger, and disappointment when things don't go according to our plan.

Therefore, we must be mindful of our projections and how they affect us. We need to understand that expectations are not always realistic and that it is okay to make mistakes and experience disappointment. By being flexible and open-minded, we create opportunities for our circumstances to serve us rather than become dependent on our labels.

Expectation

Intending to control the environment to not feel pain

Vs Reality

The environment cannot be controlled and you feel more pain as a result of failed expectations

Victimization.

Victimization is rampant in the survivor world and the world in general. Victimization occurs when something outside of yourself causes you to feel powerless and causes you pain. Now, feeling sadness and grief for a certain period makes sense. What doesn't make sense is living and reliving that scenario repeatedly and, each time, metaphorically, running yourself through the mud.

So why do we stay in our victimizations? I've observed that when someone is in "victim mode," the people around them feel sorry for them and offer them all sorts of love, affection, and attention. So, of course, it becomes addictive to stay in this place. I call these emotional offerings of love and attention "victim cuddles." So, for the sake of this book, I will refer to this phenomenon as such. It is warm and fuzzy at the time but deadly in the long run because the mood required to perpetuate the powerless state develops new neural pathways in the brain that cause you to stay stuck in victim mode.

The victim feels sadness and receives all sorts of victim cuddles. The victim feels an authentic and natural reaction of happiness and connection, so they repeatedly attempt this type of connection. Over time, the brain and body learn that this elicits a particular response that feels good so it becomes a habit or a subconscious form of manipulation.

However, this is a backward model because pain and sadness perpetuate more pain and sadness.

Additionally, we are keeping our past alive in our minds. The mind doesn't know the difference between real and perceived stress. So, in a way, you are reliving your pain to validate your craving to be loved and receive connection. Do yourself a favour and find more fulfilling ways of facilitating connection.

I know you may have been through a lot; I'm not intending to mitigate that. However, I intend to help you create a better life, and for you to have that, we need to get you out of victim mode and into empowerment mode. Yes, you may miss out on some victim cuddles (bummer), but you will get your life back: your happiness, vitality, hopefulness, appreciation, passion, confidence, body autonomy, etc. It all comes down to this.

Can it be done? Yes, without a doubt.

Does This Mean We Should Never Feel Like a Victim?

Not at all; there is undoubtedly a time and place for feeling victimized by your circumstances. When things are fresh in your experience and your expectations have been rocked, there is a transitional period where most people feel pain, sadness, anger, grief, and victimization. This is a natural reaction.

From my perspective, the only damaging practice is **staying** in victimization for weeks, months, or even years. Staying in our victimizations leads to potential depression, anxiety, and general unhappiness.

Making Positive Changes.

Stories, expectations, and victimizations differ slightly in how they influence our lives. Yet, one thread runs through all three of these concepts: They are serving you, or they are not serving you. First things first: We must identify our stories/expectations and victimizations. Then, what they fulfill. Once we have determined that we can shift our perceptions to support positive evolution.

In the following questions, I will be helping you dive into some of your stories and victimizations to help you understand the needs they fulfill. Then, we will rewrite these stories with a new (better serving) need to be fulfilled.

In the next chapter, we will be expanding on these concepts. These concepts alone have the power to change your life.

✅ **Action Step:** In your daily interactions listen to other people's stories. Notice their victimization, expectations, and stories. There is no need to point them out. Just notice of them.

📖 **Journal Questions:**

1. What are some of the more familiar stories in your life? What needs do those stories fulfill?

- *Story:* "I'm so bad at expressing my emotions."
- *Need filled:* Not having to face your emotional turmoil.

2. What are some empowering stories you could tell yourself instead and some new and attractive needs those stories could fulfill?

- *Story:* "I am emotionally well and learning to deal with my emotions."
- *Need filled:* positive improvements in close relationships and partnerships as a result.

3. What are some of your common victimizations that garner "victim cuddles"? What is a healthier way to connect and gain closeness?

- Always talking about your "story" to gain victim cuddles
- *Becomes* -> starting a support group for people with the same adversities.

ELEVEN

Practice

UNLEARNING STORIES, CHOICE, ATTITUDE, AND
LIMITING BELIEFS

This chapter is dedicated to deepening our understanding of stories, how they are formed, and how to begin combatting the stories that are not serving us. Arming ourselves with knowledge is one of the most effective tools in our toolbox. I will also give you some tools to begin to put these concepts into practice at the end of the chapter. While going through cancer, knowing and understanding these principles helped me to reshape the experiences I was going through; to turn those experiences into lessons and opportunities for growth. I hope they can help you the same way they did for me by putting these practices into real life situations.

Let's Recap.

In the last chapter, we learned that we have stories and stories run our lives. Stories are neither good nor bad; they are what they are. Stories can fuel your happiness or extinguish your joy.

Why Do We Avoid Change?

Many of us want to keep our stories the same, even if they bring us pain. Why is this?

1. It is the evil we know. There is certainty in not changing anything.
2. Changing means we must grieve the loss of something (usually a hidden desire).
3. Human connection. People love drama. It makes us relatable.
4. Being "busy," "stressed," and "sad" gives us a feeling of worthiness.

Once you realize these reasons for yourself, you will have an improved ability to get started on changing them!

Forming New Habits.

Most people believe that their circumstances determine the stories of their lives. However, the truth is that the stories we tell ourselves shape our circumstances. Once you realize this, you can begin to take control of your life. What life do you want to lead? What experiences would you like to avoid? What does your ideal life look like?

In Chapter 9, we discussed the importance of defining your goals. What are your goals? Do the stories you tell yourself support or hinder your goals? The sooner you focus on your goals and create positive stories around them, the sooner you will be able to achieve them.

Creating New Stories:

Step 1: Realize your stories (the most crucial step).

Step 2: Have compassion for yourself and our stories.

Step 3: Gather evidence for how these stories are <u>not valid.</u>

Step 4: Replace the hidden desire your story is fulfilling with more appealing aspirations.

Step 5: Repetition, repetition, repetition.

We Must Become the Authors.

If you're waiting for your life to improve before changing the stories you tell yourself, you will be waiting for a while. The truth is the stories we tell ourselves about our lives and our circumstances have a powerful impact on our perception of reality. Waiting for external circumstances to change before telling ourselves a different story is a surefire way to feel stuck and powerless in our created narrative.

So, what's the solution? Instead of waiting for life to improve, start changing your stories now. This doesn't mean you have to pretend that everything is perfect when it's not. Instead, it means making daily choices that support the new reality you want to create. You could start a gratitude practice to help shift your focus to the positive aspects of your life. Or, you could start setting small, achievable goals that help you move toward your dreams.

The key is to remember that you have the power to shape your own reality through the stories you tell yourself. Don't wait for life to improve to start telling yourself a different story. Start now, and watch as your perception of the world around you begins to shift.

Choice.

Understand that everything in life is a choice; yes, even how you deal with trauma/health/grief/life/loss. You didn't get to choose for or against what happened to you. However, you can choose whether it works for or against you. The choice is ultimately yours.

Change Your Attitude.

The attitude we adopt can significantly impact our day-to-day life. Our mental state can either encourage or discourage us from making the most of our experiences and lessons. A hopeful attitude can be a driving force that fuels our determination and guides us in achieving our goals. On the other hand, a negative attitude can cause us to see the world through a distorted lens, making us feel as though nothing we do will ever be enough. Therefore, it is crucial to approach life with a positive mindset and embrace every lesson as an opportunity for growth and self-improvement even when unfavourable. Only then can we truly make the most of what life has to offer.

What Does "Attitude" Have to Do with It?

Our attitude towards the world around us is everything. As you have seen in chapter 10. if we have many disempowering stories, we will end up with a disempowered life.

Our attitude directs the stories we draw from. If we have a poor attitude, we tend to draw from disempowering stories; alternatively, if we have a good attitude, we tend to pull from the more empowering stories.

Does This Mean You Should Be Positive All the Time?

Absolutely not; in fact, toxic positivity is equally if not more damaging than chronic negativity; ideally, it's the balance we want to strive for. Our feelings are meant to be felt. It's essential to evoke the emotions within yourself. Then, when enough time and reflection have been exercised, your attitude towards the situation can be deliberately changed to suit the changing needs of your mental growth.

What Creates a Poor Attitude?

Our upbringing often shapes our attitude, the people we interact with daily, our physical well-being, and the circumstances we have endured. We tend to let external events control our attitude, waiting for things to improve before we work on cultivating a better attitude. However, I recommend taking the opposite approach: change your attitude and you'll see your circumstances start to change with a different outlook.

How Can We Set Ourselves Up for Success?

Firstly, breaking recurring attitudes within families can be a real game changer. Many people develop a negative attitude due to their upbringing. While we can't change our past, we can choose to break the cycle of negative behaviour and generational trauma. You will have the opportunity to do so throughout the chapters.

Secondly, let's take a closer look at the people who surround you. What are their traits? How do you feel after interacting with them? Our personalities are a reflection of the company we keep, so make sure to consider this when choosing your friends. Although cutting certain people out of your life can sometimes be unrealistic, spending more time with those who brighten your day can make a real difference.

Thirdly, your physical state has a significant impact on your attitude, your choices, and your overall mental state. The following acronym is used in many addictions, mental health, and diet programs:

Hungry
Angry
Lonely
Tired.
H.A.L.T

If you are feeling any of the above, understand that your resiliency will be low. When your energy is low, it is a time for self-care, compassion, and rest. Not for progress, effectiveness, or effort. Pushing yourself to work during this time will inevitably end in a loss of optimal results.

Our Attitude Influences Our Life.

Even the micro choices you make are influenced by your attitude. Whatever you think and feel will direct your choices, decisions, opportunities, experiences, and manifestations. This phenomenon is governed by the part of the brain called the reticular activating system. This system in the brain allows you to notice things you have already focused on (ie. you buy a blue car and now you see blue cars everywhere). This system works the other way too. If you have a poor outlook on life, you will inevitably walk by opportunities you simply don't notice.

So, even the simple act of reading this book is already broadening your horizons and therefore, you will begin to see things you haven't visited in the past, leading to opportunities and potential paths to the things you want to have in your life. How exciting is that!?

What Are Limiting Beliefs?

Limiting beliefs are beliefs about yourself and the world around you that limit your efficacy in realizing your goals. For example, if you want to run a marathon but believe you are lazy, weak, and have no time, you will never run that marathon. In essence, limiting beliefs inform your limiting stories.

Limiting beliefs are often the result of our early experiences and conditioning. These experiences can come from various sources, such as our parents, guardians, family members, peers, teachers, and the wider community we grew up in. Our subconscious mind absorbs these experiences and beliefs, which can influence our thoughts, feelings, and behaviours later in life.

Another example: suppose you grew up in an environment where people constantly criticized and belittled your dreams. You may develop a belief that you are not good enough or capable of achieving success. Alternatively, if you grew up in an environment where you were praised for your dreamer tendencies, then you may believe you can and will be successful.

These core beliefs can become deeply ingrained into our subconscious mind, and we may not even be fully aware of them. These limiting beliefs inform your limiting stories determine your results. This toxic cocktail may keep us from reaching our full potential and living a fulfilling life. However, by identifying and challenging these limiting beliefs, we can overcome them and create a more positive and empowering mindset.

Making Positive Changes:

All of this may start to feel overwhelming. Don't worry; here are some tips and tricks to break it down and make the process easier. Let's discuss a few loopholes to help get you started:

- Simple repetition creates new habits. The more you repeat these new affirming stories and beliefs, the faster these beliefs will change; this can be done through daily affirmations, journalling, or reading on the subject.

- Begin to gather evidence of how your story or limiting beliefs are untrue. Curiosity challenges the limiting beliefs in a way that is none threatening to the subconscious mind.
- Identify the reward your old, outdated story gave you and replace it with a new story resulting in an even better reward.
- Surround yourself with a supportive community. The people and the environment we surround ourselves with often strongly influence our mood, attitude, beliefs, and choices. Who can you surround yourself with that will hold you accountable and inspire you to look at life more positively?
- Go within - Meditations, breathwork, visualizations. These often tap into your subconscious mind and "fast track" positive change. When we get quiet with ourselves, we can hear our intuition. *Many supportive and free meditations can be found on my website and podcast, so if intrigued feel free to take a look at those!*

✅ **Action Step:** Write down a new choice or habit that you plan to make/change and put it on your mirror.

📖 **Journal Questions:**

1. Review your outdated and unfulfilling stories answered in the last chapter and gather evidence to prove these stories are untrue.

- Story: "I'm so bad at expressing my emotions."
- Evidence: Recall times when you were emotionally intelligent.

2. Look at the new stories you have written for yourself and gather evidence on how you are already equipped to make those changes. Then, come up with ideas to fill in any gaps.

- Story: "I am emotionally well and learning to deal with my emotions."
- Evidence: Recall how you have improved over the years and what steps you have taken to enhance your emotional regulation. Then, plan out who you will source to help you fill in any gaps.

TWELVE

Renew

CULTIVATING SELF-COMPASSION

Compassion is a lost art in the hustle-and-grind culture we live in today. We have been examining our stories, beliefs, attitudes, expectations, and choices in the past few chapters. It is time to examine our ability to rest, recuperate, and process. You can look at this chapter as the "yin" to the last few chapters' "yang."

These lessons that you see here were some of the most important ones I learned from my experience with cancer. Prior to my diagnosis, I was always on the go and took pride in that fact. I thought that slowing down would make me lazy which is why I tended to disseminate and spread myself too thin; which in turn led up to achieving lackluster results while constantly feeling tired and drained. I was able to inspire rest, and I hope you find this chapter to be inspiring too.

Compassion After Challenge.

Self-compassion and rest are so tragically under-utilized today. We have created a culture of "do-do-do," and we look down on rest. Today, rest is viewed as lazy or unimportant. Yet, it is one of the most essential tools in our toolbox (if productivity and results are part of your goals).

Remember when you were a child and nap time was a non-negotiable? As soon as you were grouchy or overstimulated, the adults in the room would (hopefully) take you to a quiet place to calm down or nap. Then, after the nap, you would wake up refreshed and more clear-headed.

Alternatively, there were also times when you were a child and were in an irritable mood that your parents (who probably were also tired and needed rest) would shame you or get reactive to your moods. Ask yourself this; how did that work out for both of you? Poorly, right? Shaming and reacting with disapproval end up with an unsuccessful outcome. It didn't work then for your parent and child dynamic, and it won't work within your-self now.

So, now in your life, these dynamics come back into place into your existence. When we feel we have to "earn" our rest, we feel we don't deserve it. Then we end up putting a ton of pressure on ourselves to be productive at every given moment. The model of earning rest is backwards and isn't helping anyone. Instead, we need to work with the cycles of the ebb and flow of life.

When you decide on a goal, consider taking inspired action only when the inspiration comes, rather than "grinding" (that will end up, leaving you tired and worn down) or forcing your desired outcome. Then, when that action is beginning to cause you fatigue, plan some rest. Planning rest will ultimately allow you to be more productive in the long run, and you can complete those goals more effectively with a revived outlook.

Some examples of intentional rest might be;

- Getting proper sleep
- Walking in nature
- Yoga
- Meditation
- Art
- Bath
- Spa service
- Movie
- Date night
- etc.

Not to be confused with:

- Procrastination
- Social media scrolling
- Binge-watching
- Alcohol/Drugs

Choosing The Right Practice for You.

When it comes to finding the proper rest that fulfills your soul, it's important to ask yourself what activities or practices make you feel good. Are you someone who enjoys being creative perhaps through painting, writing, or crafting? Or do you find joy in playing music or listening to different genres. If numbers are more your thing, you might enjoy engaging in mathematical puzzles or solving equations. Alternatively, if you're sports-oriented, you might prefer engaging in activities like running, swimming, or playing a team sport. Remember that everyone's needs and preferences are different, so it's important to take the time to figure out what works best for you on your personal journey to finding soul-fulfilling rest.

Practicing Compassion for Emotional Capacity.

During different points in your life, different types of rest and compassion may be needed. Not every situation calls for a great yoga session or a healthy salad. Some situations can be so traumatic that the body wants to disassociate for a period of time, or, conversely, the situation you face may be so simple that you are ready to spring into action and get to work on changing your circumstance.

Cultivating the compassion to know where you are on the scale is a skill all on its own. I call this scale the "Hierarchy of Needs," and it refers to the skill of identifying what your body, mind, and spirit need at any given time.

Hierarchy of Needs:

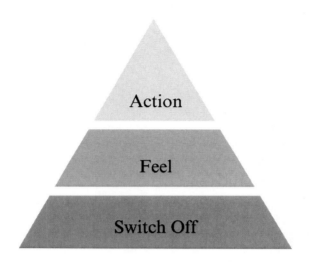

Switch Off

There are times when life gets to be too much. I get it; I've been there. Below is a list of activities that can help to give you a break from everyday stress without causing you harm in the long run by practicing destructive behaviours.

Note: The point of this list is to give you safe and effective ways of switching off when needed, but to eventually move up the hierarchy of needs to transcend overwhelm.

The need to switch off is not the absence of feeling; it is our body's reaction to too many feelings. This reaction can happen when a person faces a traumatic event or becomes extremely overwhelmed.

I know when I was first diagnosed, it was impossible to meditate or journal (which are healthy "feel it" techniques). All I could do at that time was shut off. That is why I have created this list today. So that you may not feel so alone or "broken" when you can't move into a healthy process at the sudden onset of trauma.

Examples Of Switching Off:

- Social media
- Watching TV/movies
- Sleep more
- Fiction novels
- Music/Podcasts
- Gaming
- Baths
- Take on a new hobby
- Watching comedy
- Playing with pets/animals
- Cleaning/reorganizing (controlling environment)
- Avoiding certain triggering situations

Feel It.

Taking intentional time to move our sadness or grief is essential in the healing process. When taking time to feel out emotions, consider a trained psychologist or counselor.

- Counseling, Support groups
- Crying/Screaming
- Journalling
- Symbolic release exercises (burning ceremony, writing letters, prayer, cord cutting)
- Somatic therapy
- Talking with trusted friends and family
- Tapping EFT
- Punch a pillow/Smash therapy
- Energy healing

- This list goes on and on, be true to you!

Spring Into Action.

This is when we have experienced the feelings we needed to feel and are now ready to move on from the emotions and begin to construct positive changes in our lives.

- Goal setting
- Hire a life coach
- Daily to-do lists and tasks
- Setting goals into motion/taking inspired action.

Common Mistakes.

Two common mistakes I often see when people are stressed, overworked or overwhelmed is they either remain in the "Switch off" stage in order to never have to "Feel it", or, alternatively, they skip the first two steps and move straight to action. Both have detrimental long term effects as they are essentially numbing the pain you feel. Numbing is relatable to spraying bleach on compost. It's still stinky; it can't finish its breakdown and it won't turn into the fertile soil.

Receiving Help.

Often, when we are stressed or overwhelmed, there are people around us who are willing to help. Receiving is often an over-looked skill as most of us were taught to avoid receiving because we might come off as selfish, weak, or lazy. However, when you cannot receive, it results in you being left alone and without aid.

How good are you at receiving? If someone offers you help, do you take it? Or, do you instead say: "No thanks, I got it!" for most of us, it is the latter, not the former. Consider this: If you can't receive good things from others, what makes you think you can receive good things from life? Also, you know how good it feels to help others, why deny them that?

If you turn this dynamic around and think about how much you enjoy helping and being needed by others, why do you believe you will be a bother or a burden to others?

Self-Worth.

Do you ever feel like you don't deserve help, love, or support? It's a common feeling that many of us experience and it's often rooted in a deep sense of unworthiness. The reasons behind this inferiority can vary greatly from one person to another. For some, it might stem from childhood trauma, perhaps having parents that were especially hard on their child. For others, it could be the pressure to succeed and meet society's high expectations of perfection and success.

Regardless of the reason, the result is often the same: a low sense of self-worth and a tendency to take on too much. This can cause a lot of pain not only for you but also for those who genuinely want to help you. Imagine if you repeatedly tried to assist someone you love, only to have them reject your help every time. Eventually, you might start to feel undervalued and unimportant.

It's important to remember that you are worthy of love and support simply because you exist. You don't need to prove your worth to anyone. You are enough as you are. If you're struggling with this issue, know that you're not alone. It's okay to ask for help and to let others support you. In fact, it's a sign of strength, not weakness.

So, the next time someone offers to help you, consider accepting their offer. You deserve love, help, and support, and there's nothing wrong with accepting it.

Becoming Present to Release Suffering.

Practicing the art of becoming present can be an effective tool for alleviating stress and feelings of overwhelm. One of the most effective ways to do that is by learning the skill of becoming present. In today's world, we are so consumed with our daily lives that we often forget to take a moment to appreciate our surroundings and to be mindful of the current moments taking place. By living in the past or worrying about the future, we rob ourselves of the opportunity to experience joy and contentment.

Have you ever found yourself in survival mode, struggling to remember all the things you needed to do that day? This is because your mind is preoccupied and continuously racing, leaving you unable to focus and be present. Unfortunately, many people live their entire lives like this, with a stress fog that hovers around them, making it impossible to tap into their own intuition and inner knowing.

When you become present and aware of the current moment, you free yourself from this stress fog. Being present helps you to focus and you can see more clearly and think more rationally. You become more aware of your surroundings and can make better decisions.

Therefore, it is essential to practice becoming present regularly. You can do this by taking a few deep breaths, pausing to appreciate your surroundings, or meditating. Remember, it's the little things that matter, and by being present, you can make a big difference in your life and the lives of those around you.

These simple practices detailed in this chapter can transform your life experience simply by helping you to exit survival mode. We all have an inner intelligence to heal ourselves, or to access our brilliance and brave our fears. However, most of us are running around stressed and on autopilot. This turns off our creativity and resourcefulness. So, the next time you feel tempted to skip rest and relaxation, do yourself a favour and prioritize rest in the interest of effective productivity

---

☑ **Action Step**: Set aside time this week for intentional rest. It can be 10 minutes of reading your favorite book or perhaps taking in a spa appointment. Either way, feed your soul the rest it deserves!

📖 **Journal Questions**:

1. Think of someone close to you to whom you often show compassion. Consider how you offer them compassion and encourage them to take intentional rest. What are some phrases you use to support this person?

> Example: "Don't worry about it, [Name]. You need to take care of yourself! If you need a night off, take it!"

2. Rewrite one of the most common phrases you say to this person for yourself. Notice any feelings that arise as you write this.

3. What are some of your favourite practices that fulfill you mentally and physically? What activities bring you joy and ignite your passion? Examples may include painting, fishing, singing, being active, bathing, or working outside. Create a comprehensive list of these activities, which you can refer to when you need rest and relaxation.

THIRTEEN

Vitalize

REVITALIZING YOUR BODY AFTER CHALLENGE, CHANGE, DISEASE OR BURNOUT

What would this book be without touching on the physical healing aspect? After all, healing is mind, *body*, and spirit. In this chapter, we will be discussing the physical healing aspect of health.

When the body is sick, overworked, or overwhelmed for long periods, that can take a toll on the body. After chemotherapy, radiation, and surgery, my body was left feeling sick, worn out, touched out, riddled with side effects, energetically dense, bloated, beat up, and exhausted.

I felt angry. I had so many side effects and my body was feeling raw and agitated. The last thing I wanted to do was eat well and exercise. I had to begin slowly and give myself a massive dose of compassion.

Below is a list of things I did to heal my physical body post-cancer. Maybe you have been through a long season of feeling beat up physically, too. If you are feeling like a stranger in your body, if you feel worn down and tired, if you need vitality and health in your life; this list will apply to you.

1. Exercise/ Physical Activity:

When most of us have been down and out for some time, exercise falls to the side. To begin again, start with gentle activities and gradually progress. Incorporate exercises like walking, stretching, or yoga, gradually increasing intensity as strength improves. Patience is key—listen to your body and progress comfortably. Remind yourself repeatedly that something is better than nothing. Comparing yourself to others or the "old you" will keep you in a shame loop. You may start with five minutes a day only, and that's okay; there is no limit to progression.

I started with walking. Walking is unbelievably healing and is low impact yet practical for the body. It is also highly effective at warding off diseases and disease recurrence. Adding oxygen to our tissues through gentle movement can reduce inflammation, protect the joints, and strengthen our cardiovascular health without taxing the body and cortisol levels (which some more intense exercises do).

Then, with time and patience, I began lifting light weights. This low-impact, bone-supporting exercise effectively rebuilt the muscle I had lost. I started low and went slow. Exercise took time and wasn't always as easy to implement. However, with time, it became fun!

Lately, I have begun yoga classes again. It took me years to rebuild my strength and I finally decided to get back into yoga. I love yoga because it is a mind, body, and spirit exercise. I find it centering and enjoyable.

Exercise is not a one-size-fits-all approach. I prefer relaxed, low-impact exercises that I can do at home. At the same time, others may prefer the high energy of a spin or dance class.

Whatever your interest is, it must be unique to you individually for you to stick with it.

Rule #1: Start low and go slow.

Rule #2: Choose an exercise you enjoy rather than what you think you "should do"

2. Nutrition for Recovery:

Nutrition plays a pivotal role in rebuilding health. Yet, many people turn this exciting opportunity into fear, judgment, and shame. The diet industry fuels this. We have been conditioned to see food as "good" or "bad" rather than viewing it instead as fuel or simply pleasure. Unfortunately, this is perpetuated by the constant rhetoric that being skinny is more important than being healthy.

I know when I was first diagnosed, I received unsolicited advice from so many people regarding my eating habits and the onset of cancer or cancer recurrence, which is ironic as I was obsessed with eating healthy before cancer. I had been on several "no sugar," "no carbohydrate," "no GMO," "no non-organic," "no alcohol," and "no chemical/processed" diets before cancer.

I became obsessed with following everyone's advice. I took everyone's suggestions, read books, watched videos online, and scoured the internet for advice. Over time, the lists began to contradict themselves. Some foods had research to support they caused cancer and then those same foods would have research that proved they prevented cancer. My head was spinning and my mental health began to suffer.

I then chose to throw away all the conflicting advice and instead focus on what felt right to me. Of course, through my research,

I had a pretty good idea of some of the cancer "superfoods" and, therefore, had my staple foods. However, I began building an understanding of myself and my beliefs alongside it.

I started instead seeing food as fuel or pleasure rather than "good" or "bad." This helped me to avoid the cycle of completely cutting out certain foods and then bingeing on them later when my willpower broke.

So, here is my invitation: Instead of cutting out foods that may be "bad," focus on adding healthy, revitalizing foods and watch your energy begin to restore. Ask yourself the question: "Do I feel good in my body when I eat this food?" and choose based on the answer. Sometimes the answer may be: "Even though my body doesn't feel good eating this food, I would instead like to enjoy the pleasure of eating it" If so, then enjoy the food without shame or judgment; you might find the food feels different in your body.

3. Managing Fatigue:

Fatigue is so common in the world today. We have an epidemic of underslept, over-performing adults. Our diseases are skyrocketing and mental health is in crisis. In this section, I will attempt to give you the tools that I personally used to heal my fatigue.

Fatigue can be utterly debilitating. There were some days when I couldn't get out of bed in the morning and some nights I wouldn't sleep a wink because of the steroids. I felt lazy and I felt inefficient. It was challenging to do simple things; exercise and eating well seemed to sink to the bottom of my list.

I searched and searched to find the reason for my fatigue so that I could mitigate it. What I found was two factors: the amount of **quality** sleep I got and the amount of stress I was under. I got to work improving my sleep hygiene and worked on my mindset, and like magic, my energy began to return. Let's discuss further about what I did below:

Sleep Habits to Improve Quality of Sleep:

- Turn the lights down 2-4 hours before sleep
- No digital devices 2-4 hours before sleep
- Stop eating or only eating easy-to-digest foods 2-4 hours before sleep
- Soft music/ Meditations/ Breathwork
- Gratitude practice
- Reading/ Journalling before bed
- Comfortable mattress topper/ good pillows/ Cool the room down/Cooling gel foam
- Warm tea, hot water before bed
- Supplements (ask health care practitioner first)

Once I was able to improve the quality of my sleep my energy began to return. Then, I added gentle movement and nutrition, and my energy is now normal. It truly is a mind, body, and spirit approach.

Tips to Help with Stress:

Explore complementary therapies such as

- Acupuncture
- Body talk
- Reiki
- Journalling/Meditation
- Massage
- Chiropractic care
- Moving meditation (Yoga, walking)
- Prayer
- Breathwork

- Visualizations
- Activities that give you a feeling of "flow" or relaxation (IE, painting, piano, knitting)

These modalities can alleviate physical discomfort, reduce stress, and support the body's natural healing processes.

4. Rediscovering Connection to Your Body:

When our bodies and minds go through something traumatic, we often lose the connection to our bodies. We may have turned towards sexuality as a coping mechanism or turned away. We may be struggling to be present with ourselves and our partners both sensually and sexually, and we may be left with poor body image because of emotional eating or abstaining from food. In any instance, this can become a painful and disheartening subject.

In my circumstance, being on anti-hormone medication directly attacked my sexuality. I was left without a libido; I had vaginal atrophy, hot flashes, and loss of sensation, and I gained 35 pounds; I couldn't stand the sight of myself in the mirror. I had no interest in showing my body to my husband. I felt lost, ashamed, and like a failure as a wife and partner. I was concerned for my marriage and I was terrified I would never return to a normal and healthy place.

I began researching anything and everything I could about the subject. I worked with a pelvic floor specialist, Ob/gyn, nurse practitioners, and menopause clinics. They all helped me marginally, but not as much as I had hoped. It wasn't until one day when I was listening to a podcast about weight loss medications, that the speaker said a sentence that forever changed my life and the way I view my body.

The podcast host said: "The body holds chemicals like chemo-therapy in the fat tissues to draw them away from the body's vital organs." Upon hearing these words, I broke down crying. I had spent my entire life hating my body for being larger, punishing it with diets and unrealistic exercise goals; I thought it was ugly, dirty, and undeserving of pleasure because it was large, and yet, all this time, it was trying to keep me safe.

The tears flowed. I held my body and apologized. I began to see her as a small girl, trying her best to make me (the parent) happy and satisfied with her actions. I apologized for making her feel unloved and undervalued. I forgave her for not being able to deliver the skinny person I so desperately wanted to be. I released the extremely high standards that I had set for her.

I call my realization "body neutrality" because although I had not discovered authentic "body positivity" for the larger body I now have, I was able to cultivate gratitude for my body's ability to heal, live, process food, and keep me safe. That was a massive step from self-loathing to understanding. Since that day, all aspects of sexuality/ sensuality/ body image has improved for me. Not every day is perfect, but there have been huge strides in the positive direction.

When it comes to your body, I believe it can feel your discon-tentment/ anger/ judgment or disgust towards it. I believe our bodies respond to our minds. Do yourself a favour; begin to see your body for what it is: a miracle that is trying its best to keep you safe.

You don't have to love the fat cells; that is not required. Hell, I don't! Instead, if you can look past that, look deeper and find gratitude for the body that you have, for all it's abilities to love, touch, hold, digest, experience etc. and watch it heal and begin to serve you without fear.

In Conclusion:

Regaining physical vitality in your body is a gradual process that demands patience, dedication, and personalized care. Individuals can embark on a journey towards renewed physical well-being by understanding the body's needs, incorporating healthy lifestyle choices, embracing a holistic approach to healing, and learning to cultivate body neutrality.

☑ **Action Step**: Stand on front of the mirror (clothing optional) and thank each part of your body for what it does for you.

📖 **Journal Questions**:

1. Write a list of as many things as you can think of that you love about your body.
2. Write a list of ten of your favorite stress relieving activities that you can draw from when you are feeling stressed or worn out.

FOURTEEN

Solidify

IDENTITY AND INTERPRETATION

What is your self-identity? Who do you see yourself as? Are you a happy, motivated, and health-oriented individual? Or do you consider yourself lazy, sluggish, and unsuccessful? Your self-identity is crucial as it determines your results in all aspects of life. If you wish to regain your health, lose weight or change your habits, you must alter your self-identity.

How can you do that? By telling yourself a different story! You must be mindful of the words you use to describe yourself and your actions since they will dictate your current and future success. As you change your story (and, therefore, your self-identity), you will gradually begin to perceive the world around you from a different perspective. If you combine this with a healthy dose of compassion, you are bound to succeed.

During my battle with cancer, I had to start considering myself as someone who was completely healed. This shift in self-identity helped me persevere through the toughest of days because over time I genuinely started to believe that I was fully healed. Naturally, there were moments when I felt like giving up but my self-identity kept me going.

What Have You Learned as A Result of Your Experiences?

Everyone has their own story whether it's cancer, divorce, career change, loss of a pet or loved one, etc. Everyone has a choice after those experiences have been endured. The identity we take on due to our experiences has everything to do with our quality of life going forward. Those experiences may have been challenging and awful, leaving you feeling tired. However, do you want those thoughts to dominate your mind or do you want to move on by letting go and being happy?

Assuming that your answer is to "be happy," we must change some identity beliefs around your journey. Instead of "X happened **to** me". Let's change the narrative: "X happened *for* me" it's a hard pill to swallow, I know. However, Everything we encounter has an opportunity for expansion, and it's up to us to find it.

The experiences that happen to us are designed to shift us into a broader and more expressed version of ourselves. Consider this imagery: if you're not listening, God throws a pebble, and if you're still not listening, God throws a rock, and if you're continually not listening, God throws a boulder. Meaning, the events that happen in our lives are designed to shift us. However, if we aren't listening then we may be given another lesson. You have an opportunity to grow, shift, and evolve with every challenge thrown your way. What will you choose?

Questions to ask yourself to identify potential gifts that may have come from your challenges in life:

- Am I happier now?
- Had I truly enjoyed my life before the event? How about now?
- Did I do too much for others? Has that changed?

- Did I put too many people before myself? Has that changed?
- Did I hide my light from the world? Stay small? Has that changed?
- Did I live in my purpose? Enjoy my work? Has that changed?

What determines your success or failure in happiness, in all areas of life, is how you choose to view it.

I can hear you asking: "OK, Christine, I hear you; but I'm sick of learning lessons... When will they stop?"

Answer: "They won't stop, but our pain response can stop. You will always have within you what you need to get through"

Make The Choice.

Most of the suffering and outcomes in our lives, with some exceptions, are a result of the choices we make. We can choose how we perceive and interpret any given situation and the choices we make will ultimately determine our results and our happiness.

I understand that some things may not feel like a choice or within your control, such as your financial situation, health, relationships, body, or friendships. However, all of these are a result of choices we have made prior and can be changed with new choices moving forward. Your ability to discern, detach, and decide to change your situation will define your future. The way you choose to view the situation will determine whether it serves you or not.

I encourage you to make a conscious choice today to allow your story to propel you forward to becoming the person you aspire to be!

Resistance to Positive Change.

Let's discuss the concept of resistance to the good things in life. Many of us don't realize that we often resist what we truly desire. This resistance stems from the fact that something requires releasing in order to manifest our desires. Think about where in your life you may be resisting moving forward due to fear. Are you afraid of failure? Losing people in your life? Change? Feeling like you need more?

Making profound changes in your life can be uncomfortable and fearful. You must step beyond your comfort zone to get to where you want to be. I understand this feeling all too well. After my battle with cancer, I had to continually put myself out there, hoping that people would find my work valuable. It was terrifying to be so vulnerable.

With time, my self-worth grew and my actions felt more natural. Showing up took bravery and your goals will require the same of you. No matter what you desire, your tendency to avoid frightening situations in order to gain comfort, certainty, and pleasure will have to shift. This is the breakdown before the change that we've been discussing.

What's on the other side of that discomfort? Everything you've ever wanted, of course!

Concept Into Practice:

1. Don't wait until you feel entirely ready to chase your goals because you may never feel completely ready. Start taking action towards your goals. It's okay to feel unsure or unprepared; in fact, it's completely normal. However, it's important to remember that the only way to achieve your goals is to start taking gradual action,

no matter how small the steps may be. This action will create clarity for your next steps as they unfold.

2. Take responsibility for your shortcomings without judgment. Be honest with yourself. Acknowledge your past mistakes and take ownership of them. It's easy to blame external factors or other people for our failures but it's essential to recognize that we are ultimately responsible for our actions and decisions. By personally taking responsibility, we learn from our mistakes and move forward positively.

3. Decide to change and take small steps, one at a time. Focus on one area of your life that you want to improve, and set small, achievable goals to work towards. Over time, these small steps will add up and lead to significant progress.

4. Keep your promises to yourself. Building trust in yourself through honesty will positively affect your confidence. It's easy to make promises to ourselves, but it's often harder to keep them. Start by setting small goals and promises, and make sure to follow through on them. By doing so, you'll develop a sense of self-trust and confidence that will help you achieve your larger goals.

The key to achieving your dreams is to stop waiting for the perfect time to start and take action. Start small, be consistent, and push yourself out of your comfort zone. By taking ownership of your past mistakes, setting small goals, and keeping promises to yourself, you can build self-trust and confidence that will help you achieve your goals and realize your future dreams making them your reality.

Personal Responsibility.

So many of us want various things but never even begin because we believe it "isn't in the cards for us" or we have too many limitations. Trust me when I say most of those limitations are simple challenges you can overcome with effort, determination, and belief. I used to think there was a "pie in the sky" that determined who was meant to be successful and who wasn't. I don't believe that anymore. The further I move into my career, the more I realize consistency, determination, fluidity, a willingness to learn and belief in yourself are the only determining factors in one's successes or failures.

Let's be honest here. When trying to change our lives, we all have some "bad" (non-expansive) habits. When you get real with yourself and take responsibility for these facts, you can forgive and move on. It is all about the awareness of those habits and the intention to move forward. It's not about becoming unphased or proficient at not having them! If you are waiting for that, you'll be here for a long time, my friend.

I get it; some challenges/ roadblocks are brutal. You are allowed to feel low, to be the victim in your story for some time. However, there comes a time when you have to make a choice. Do you want to shift with the changing tides or do you instead want to identify as your struggles? Because there is no wrong answer but there will be consequences to what you choose.

If you desire positive change, you must transcend your limitations. It's as simple as that. If you decide to change with the process of re-empowering yourself you will grow to new heights you never thought possible. If instead you choose comfort, you will remain where you are. Comfortable but not moving forward. That's ok, too. But be aware of the consequences of that choice and be ready to accept your chosen path without judgment.

Decision - Commitment.

When you make the decision to commit to something, it's important to understand that a part of your brain will inevitably try to stop you. This is because your brain is wired to protect you from potential harm or pain. It's a natural response that helps you stay safe and avoid danger. The brain doesn't understand the difference between real danger and let's say a career change so it reacts the same way it would if you were being chased.

When a feeling like this arises, it's important to not ignore nor push it away. Instead, it's best to allow it to be present and acknowledge what it is: fear. It's important to wait for this fear to come up like a cat patiently waiting outside a mouse's hole. When it does, greet it with kindness and curiosity. Say to yourself, "Oh, hello, self-doubt! How are you feeling today?"

By being self-aware and acknowledging these fears, we can now begin to change the fear itself. We can learn to understand why we feel this way and move past it. We can start to recognize that fear is a natural part of life and it doesn't have to hold us back from achieving our goals.

Remember, it's through self-awareness that we can learn to overcome our fears and grow as individuals. So, don't be afraid to face your fears and embrace the challenges that come with committing to something new.

Make Friends with Change.

As a society, it would serve us much better to move away from "I'd like to, but it's hard" and start moving towards "I'd like to, and I know it's going to be hard, but I'm going to do it anyway." It is our fear of discomfort that has kept us stuck.

Unfortunately, in today's culture, it is also widely accepted to bypass becoming uncomfortable or having to put effort into changing our circumstances. An example of this may be "It's not in the cards for me" or " It's a sign from the universe." I apologize to be all in your face here but these are simply "stories" we are telling ourselves that become good excuses to quit. It means you can relieve discomfort and no longer have to try.

Consider this: *If you feel discomfort, you are on the other side of a breakthrough!* Decide to alternatively make the intentional choice to go into discomfort, provided the outcome is desired. Once you make the decision, understand that you are going to falter. On your journey to success, you will need to choose again and again and again. The sooner you master this self-compassion, the sooner you can get to work!

What Does Your Dream Need from You?

We all have aspirations and objectives in life but it's important to consider what our dreams demand from us. If you want to lead a happy and fulfilling life, it's essential to understand that achieving your dreams requires effort, commitment, and sacrifice on your part. In other words, something you are currently doing needs to be shed away to make room for the new thing you desire.

For instance, if your dream is to start a business, you may need to be prepared to invest your time, energy, and resources to make it happen. You may need to conduct market research, develop a business plan, secure funding, hire employees, build a website, and create a marketing strategy. You may also need to enhance your skills, attend business classes, and network with other entrepreneurs to gain valuable insights and support.

If your dream is to heal from an illness or injury, you may need to work closely with your healthcare provider to create a treatment plan that addresses your specific needs and goals. You may need to take medications and supplements, undergo physiotherapy or other medical procedures, and make lifestyle changes to promote healing and recovery.

Suppose your desired outcome is to repair a damaged relationship. In that case, you may need to begin to communicate openly and honestly with the other person, listen to their perspective, and work together to find a resolution. You may need to seek the help of a professional counselor or mediator to facilitate the process and ensure that both parties feel heard and respected.

Achieving your dreams is not always easy and it may require you to step out of your comfort zone and face challenges and obstacles along the way. But if you stay committed to your goals, work hard, and stay positive, you can overcome any adversity and make your dreams a reality.

Self-Integrity.

What is self-integrity? Self-integrity is keeping your word true to yourself and others.

Let me ask: when you tell someone you will do something, do you do it? Most of the time, the answer is yes. There are exceptions: sickness, unforeseen circumstances, honouring your mental health needs, etc. However, when we say we will do something for someone, we do it.

Let me ask you another question: Do you follow through when telling yourself you will do something? If you are like many people, the answer is no. You break promises to yourself daily. What do you think that tells your brain? It tells your brain that you will not follow through so what's the point? When you do not follow through, the brain perceives this lack of integrity as boken self trust.

When self-trust is broken, the body and mind lose momentum. you start to feel bad about yourself and stop doing things so you won't have the opportunity to "fail" anymore. Sound familiar?

Well, trust me when I say you are not the first and you certainly won't be the last person to live without integrity to yourself. It stopped me in my tracks when I first learned about this revelation. How could I have not seen this? How could I have not seen how self-sabotaging this is?

Now you know too. Let us live in integrity for others and ourselves. Your self-trust may be broken right now but it can be mended rest assured. The unique part about this is that integrity becomes easier as you build your trust muscle! Why? Because of your commitment, the mind and body begin to trust again. This creates less internal resistance.

Consider this visualization tool:

Picture your decisions as a door, when you close the door the decision is made. In addition to closing the door, make the door disappear. So that you cannot go back on your decisions. If you can't go back, you won't go back! If you need to make a slight change, you pivot but know you cannot return.

Set Yourself Up for Success:

- Build time to rest and relax so you don't burn out.
- Employ an accountability buddy (a friend who keeps you accountable to your goals).
- Follow things and people that make you feel expansive.
- Invest in self-reflection tools such as courses, books, podcasts, etc. The learning is never done because you are ever-evolving!
- Write down your intentions and post them everywhere!

- Join masterminds and groups and create supportive circles to cheer you on!
- Have a calendar with check marks or stickers to see your progress.

✅ **Action Step**: Set up a calendar that you will measure your progress with check marks for stickers, try to achieve progress for at least 80% of each month. For example: If you hope to work out x3 days a week and you complete that goal you have achieved 100% of your goal. the goal of 80% or more keeps you in integrity.

📖 **Journal Questions**:

1. Consider a goal you have had for a long time; take some time to reflect on the goal and your personal responsibility for the ways that goal has not come to fruition. In what ways have you held back from going all in? In what ways have you been non integral to yourself and created resistance? Take your time and do not judge yourself.

2. Make a plan to hold yourself accountable to your goal. Utilize one of the tips above and create a system to hold yourself accountable!

FIFTEEN

Empower

THE ART OF SELF-EMPOWERMENT

We all have the desire to feel empowered. True empowerment comes from taking action not acquiring knowledge. However, I find that there is a unique trick that I'm excited to share with you in this chapter. This lesson was particularly significant in my cancer journey, especially during my last weeks of active treatment. During that time, I was eager to show up in the world differently and break free from the expectations of others. While I didn't need to go through cancer to make this change, I took advantage of the opportunity it presented. We can all transform ourselves at any moment.

Who Do You Want to Be?

We all have the power to shape our identity, yet we often hold ourselves back for fear of what others might think. We tend to hide our true selves to please others, which is really unfortunate. The fear of not being liked is the greatest obstacle that comes in the way of living our truth.

Who would you want to be if you could be anyone or do anything you wanted? Would you like to be more confident, sexy, powerful, or unapologetic? It's about changing who you are at your core if that's what you want. It's about taking the best parts of yourself and amplifying those traits.

In essence, how can you stop diminishing your potential? In what ways would you like to show up? What additions can you make to the beautiful person you already are?

Introducing The Alter Ego.

The role of the "alter ego" is to collapse the timeline of the goal you have in mind for yourself. You achieve this by accessing the version of yourself that has already reached your goal. An example of this is Clark Kent, whose alter ego is Superman. Accessing this version gives you the empowerment needed to take the necessary action. For example, say you want to speak on stage and tell your story but are uncomfortable with public speaking. Employing the alter ego of someone confident in public speaking helps you to transcend the fear because it simply doesn't exist within your alter ego.

Changing your ego is about switching the light switch on and showing up as your authentic self. Learn to communicate your needs and desires, learn to set boundaries, and learn how to show up big for yourself.

Did you notice I said, "Show up big as yourself?" This may sound confusing since I'm using the term "alter ego". The alter ego term may sound like I am implying you should change everything about yourself when I intend to convey the opposite. Instead, it is an invitation to turn up the volume on all your amazing qualities.

Who are you under your limiting beliefs and insecurities? Most of us have forgotten who we truly are because life has taught us that it isn't safe to be fully expressed. If you are unsure of who that fully expressed person is; recall who you were when you were a young child. Were you wild? Goofy? Studious? Or even bossy?

This will give you a starting clue as to who the true you is. To further clarify who you desire to be, and ought to express: think of a person, friend, celebrity, or family member you adore. Someone who fills your cup when you are around them. How would you describe them? Your answer probably closely describes the type of person you have within yourself!

If it is desired by you, it means that it is already within you. For example, if you love fashion, shopping, luxury, and lavishness you probably don't desire a minimalist lifestyle out in the country, right? This example serves to show you that what you desire aligns with your beliefs, values, and wants. Therefore, it is destined for you! You simply have to know how to employ it.

Your alter ego often lies somewhere between the childhood version of you and the person you adore; I know for myself I would have described my childhood self as light-hearted, upbeat, and bubbly. The person whom I adore is a friend of mine who has the most fantastic confidence. therefor, my alter ego is light-hearted and confident.

Who is that person for you? Who is the version of yourself fully embodied, without fear or doubt? The version of you that can do, be, and have anything she/he wants. This is an exciting idea for many, however, when they begin putting it into practice, they quickly learn there is a massive fear of being "too much" or "too different" from others. So, they retract.

Let's consider the person you described above...

The person you mentioned above, why do they fill your cup? My guess is they are (in one way or another) authentically themselves, correct? Perhaps you would describe them as unapologetic? Confident? Larger than life? - Am I correct? If so, then, what makes you think you are shrinking yourself for others serving them?

I'm not talking about fake confidence; fake confidence comes off as polarizing to other people and it depletes you. Fake confidence is easy to spot. These folks are loud, vain, obnoxious, unkind, erratic, self-serving, and competitive; this is not true confidence. True confidence is genuine, non-competitive, inclusive, uplifting, and magnetic. This type of confidence lifts others and allows them to express themselves fully!

How to Create Your Alter Ego:

Ask yourself the questions below and dream up your alter ego.

1. What will this alter ego *do* for you? What benefits will you enjoy as a result?
2. Give this alter ego a name...
3. What is the personality of your alter ego? (Confident, brave, strong-willed, funny, etc.)
4. Who are you modeling this alter ego after? Write out what this person is like.
5. Get a clear picture of the person you are creating. What are their favourite hobbies? What do they do for fun? What are some of their best attributes?
6. How does your alter ego dress?
7. Choose a talisman for your alter ego. A talisman is an item that makes you feel like you are your alter ego. Ex: White coat for a doctor.

The final step is to channel this person into situations that benefit you. Show up as this person when you need to access this side of yourself. Most people also find wearing, holding, or having a talisman helpful. For example, a doctor wears a white coat. This is their talisman. Choose a talisman that helps you to become the alter ego!

Tip: If you are uncomfortable, you are on the right track!

I mean this: Showing up for yourself doesn't mean you no longer have fear. Sitting in discomfort takes guts and bravery. However, bravery isn't the absence of fear; it is seeing the fear, feeling it, and doing it anyway. So, I now ask you: Are you ready to be brave?

Begin To Practice This Skill (that's right, it's a skill):

- Surround yourself with other people who fill your cup and you feel comfortable being fully expressed with.
- Fake it till you make it. Practice, practice, practice.
- Affirmations and reminders.
- Courses on growth and self-love
- Exercise and eat well (not for vanity but for self-care)
- Realize that you are magnificent and have pure potential. Every day, realize what a blessing it is to be alive and don't waste another minute not living your life to the fullest.

Your Alter Ego and Decisions.

Your alter ego knows what they want. They are your full expression without fear, doubt, and anxiety. Decision-making comes easily as you consider your needs first; this might feel selfish at first but prioritizing your needs teaches others how to treat you. Of course, there is always room for flexibility and the consideration of others. That it doesn't need to be to your detriment is key here.

Consider that the inability to decide on what you want stems from being unable to receive. Somewhere along the line, you lost the awareness of your desires because you were always focused on other people's needs. Don't worry! Decisiveness is a skill you can cultivate. With time and practice, it can become as easy as breathing.

Your Alter Ego and Boundaries.

When you begin to show up in a big way for yourself, boundaries become easy and more natural. I used to believe that boundaries were aggressive in nature. I saw boundaries as some type of confrontation you have to have where everyone leaves feeling defeated. I have since noticed that when you respect yourself and know that you deserve respect from others, people naturally offer you more respect and take advantage of you less.

This phenomenon can be explained through the science of human mirroring. Other people will mirror your state of mind; if your state of mind is that you are not valuable, people will not treat you as such. The basic principle is that your state of mind will be reflected in the world through your body posture, eye movements, and tone of voice. If you feel happy, confident, and at ease, others will treat you with kindness, reverence, and respect. However, if you feel low self-esteem, low self-worth, and no confidence, people will, without meaning to, take advantage of your willingness to give of yourself to your detriment.

Shifting your self-perception will certainly shift the way the world treats you. It's really that simple. However, there may be times when someone asks too much of you regardless. I have created a list of helpful "go-to" phrases for these people to easily set boundaries.

Helpful "Go-To" Phrases for Boundaries:

- Sorry, I can't, I need some mental health time.
- Since XYZ, this is no longer my priority, but thank you.
- Sorry, I can't. I need some time to refill my cup.

- "It doesn't feel right to me to _____"
- "It feels right to me to _____ "
- "Let me think about this and get back to you"
- "I'm so grateful for your advice, but I'm going to try something else"
- "Thanks for the feedback"
- "I know I already said yes, but I had not considered the other things I have going on, I'll need to raincheck this one"
- "I would be happy to help, but I need a day or two to prepare."

Releasing The Identity of the Giver.

Do you feel a sense of importance when you give to others? Do you sometimes give to a fault, to your own detriment? I know I did and I hated feeling like a doormat.

It's natural to want to help others and be part of a community. Giving is healthy and part of a balanced life. However, when you give too much of yourself, it can become unbalanced and you may start to resent others for taking advantage of you. This is known as being a "people pleaser." People pleasers often have low self-worth and give too much in the hopes of receiving love and attention from others that they cannot give themselves.

The compulsion to give too much often stems from not feeling essential or valued when we were young. Perhaps you were praised for being a "good boy/girl" when you pleased your parents, but criticized as "selfish" when expressing your needs and wants. This habit can become a way to gain love and approval in adulthood. If this sounds familiar, then you might be a giver who created a sense of importance around how much you could give others.

Earlier in the book, I mentioned the "Cancer personality," often associated with people-pleasing. When I learned this, it stopped me in my tracks and I realized that I was indeed a people pleaser. Nevertheless, I started working on it and I'm healing every day by working through it. I believe you can too!

Adversity can help break the mold of the "giver" mindset. Your challenges can be a blessing in disguise, allowing you to break free from this pattern. As you heal and grow, remember these lessons and implement them in your daily life.

Indeed, some people in your life may not appreciate the new you with your newly set boundaries and self-respect. But if you stay true to yourself, those who don't respect your boundaries will fall away, leaving only those who truly care about you.

✅ **Action Step:** Choose a talisman representing this alter ego and try on the alter ego at an event or gathering. Observe how others light up at your confidence.

📖 **Journal Questions:**

1. What will creating this Alter Ego **do** for you? What benefits will you enjoy as a result?

2. Give this Alter Ego a name, personality traits, and a style.

SIXTEEN

Attune

OUR MOST POWERFUL EMOTION FOR HEALING

Adversity reshapes our perspectives and the seed of gratitude lies within it. This chapter explores the transformative power of gratitude and its ability to influence the energetics of your world. Adversity often casts a shadow, yet within it lies an opportunity to feel gratitude and cultivate silver linings. Embracing gratitude involves recognizing even the tiniest glimmers of positivity amidst challenges. It's about acknowledging the lessons learned and the strength that's gained from difficult experiences.

Gratitude is the highest vibration of emotion out there. It is the end-all, be-all of manifestation and attraction of things you want in your life. If we can find gratitude in our pain, we can use this to transcend our experiences and access our power.

Gratitude.

Gratitude is a skill created and refined through conscious practice. Think of it like a muscle; the more you use it, the more natural it becomes. Becoming grateful for your challenges and roadblocks in life has a beautiful side effect of lightening your mental load, regaining perspective, and freeing you from victimhood.

Many of us get caught up in our victimizations, failed expectations or lack thereof. Victimization becomes an attitude, which eventually becomes an automatic personality. Gratitude frees us from the bonds of despair and allows us to see the world in a new light.

Think of cultivating gratitude as a metaphor for walking down a new, undiscovered grassy path. At first, walking across this grass will make little to no impact but if you continually walk the same path, it will become a worn and smooth path that will become the easiest and most walked path. Gratitude is that metaphor; the more you practice, the easier and more permanent the pathway becomes.

Shifting Perspectives.

Adversity reframes our outlook on life. We become jaded and our perspective on life becomes foggy. Gratitude acts as a clear lens, shifting focus from what was lost to what remains. It helps you to acknowledge the present moment, fostering an appreciation for the things that are often taken for granted—health, relationships, or simple pleasures. Expressing gratitude during challenging times aids in emotional healing. It doesn't negate the pain but serves as a beacon of hope by seeing the positives within the negatives.

Becoming grateful can turn your pain into power all on its own. Finding reason that your adversity has given you purpose, what good has come from it, and shifting your perception of the event disconnects you from the yearning for what you wanted (and ultimately didn't get) while opening up to the possibility that this, or something better, is coming.

Expectation: The Thief of Joy.

Expectations are an attempt at controlling your environment. Let's say you decide you want something and try to control how that thing will come to you. Then, when life seems to "turn left instead of right," you become angry that the universe isn't on your side.

The problem with this is God is always on your side. Every experience ("good" or "bad") has an opportunity for you to get closer to what you want. The problem is we define a situation as "bad" and have no gratitude for what the situation taught us; therefore, we put our blinders on. We walk by all our blessings and potential (grumbling about how life isn't fair the whole way) and miss every opportunity. In essence, we are keeping ourselves stuck.

That doesn't mean everything that happens to you feels like a blessing. Such terrible things happen in this world—terrible and unforgivable things. I wish suffering weren't an inevitability of life, but it is the human experience. I do know for sure that my terrible experience had a blessing in it for me. Others lose their lives to cancer and I have to believe in those instances that it was a blessing for their soul in some way we do not understand yet within our limited human perspective.

In our despair, this is where gratitude comes in; we take the blinders off when we cultivate gratitude in adversity. We open ourselves up to take notice of the blessings and opportunities around us, no matter how difficult. They are always there and then will we see all the stepping stones to get from where we are to where we want to be.

Growth and Resilience.

The skill of cultivating gratitude in the face of adversity is a challenging task. It requires you to let go of the victim mindset and, therefore, forgo the victim cuddles. This isn't easy as it is natural to want to be in the community and enjoy being fawned over. I get it. As a result of my people pleaser personality, I often felt alone and without aid. There are times I resent not having people take care of me. I then remind myself that I am at peace, happy, courageous, and following my purpose due to my capacity to endure, learn, and evolve, even amidst hardship. This fuels a sense of appreciation for the strength I found within.

You can also cultivate this, no matter what you are going through. This resilience from gratitude can and will set you free from your shackles and put you on the path from pain to power. If you allow it gratitude is truly one of the most potent emotions we have access to in this life.

The Energetics of Gratitude.

Gratitude is a powerful emotion that significantly attracts positive thoughts and experiences into your life. When you express gratitude, you emit a positive energy into the universe which then attracts more positive experiences, opportunities, and people into your life. This is because gratitude is a positive and a highly-vibrational emotion that aligns you with similar frequencies in the energetic field.

To understand the energetics of gratitude, you first need to recognize that everything in the universe has a vibrational frequency, including thoughts and emotions. By expressing gratitude, you send out positive energy and resonate with the positive energies in the universe. This alignment influences your personal experiences and the energetic environment around you.

In essence, while cultivating a gratitude-filled mindset you are likely to attract more to be grateful for. This practice of attuning to the energy of the world around us has been practiced for our entire human existence and has become popularized again within the last few years. I know in my life that I have seen proof of this over and over again. I have come to a place where I fully believe in this phenomenon.

Spreading Gratitude.

Expressing gratitude is an essential aspect of human connection that has the power to transform lives in countless ways. It not only benefits the person who expresses it but also has a positive impact on those around them. By sharing words of thanks or acts of kindness, you create a ripple effect that promotes positivity in the community.

Gratitude helps build connections and further deepen relationships. It fosters an environment of support where people feel valued and appreciated. When you show appreciation for someone, it can make them feel seen and heard, which can motivate them to continue doing good work.

Adopting an attitude of gratitude also has a positive impact on others. When you are in a positive state of mind, others can sense it, and they will reciprocate your positive energy back to you. This creates a cycle of reciprocal gratitude where everyone benefits from the shared positive energy.

Practicing gratitude is a powerful tool that can transform your life in beautiful ways. It can help you shift your focus from what's wrong to what's right and help you cultivate a sense of abundance and contentment in your life. By making gratitude a part of your daily routine, you can create a life that is filled with joy, love, and positivity.

✅ **Action Step**: Today, before your feet hit the floor, run through all the things that would make today great. At the end of the day, recall everything you are grateful for that made today wonderful.

📖 **Journal Questions**:

1. Write a list of things you are grateful for from A to Z. One for each letter. (Ex: A - Air to breathe).

SEVENTEEN

Connect

ENERGETICS OF EVOLUTION

Our world comprises of energy, vibration, and frequency. Every living and non-living thing in the universe, including us, has its own unique energy signature, vibration, and frequency. These three components are interconnected and have the power to influence our lives in significant ways.

Understanding the mechanics of energy, vibration, and frequency is enlightening and empowering. By learning how to align yourself with the universal flow, you can shift your current state to where you desire to be. The process of aligning with the universe is known as manifestation. Manifestation involves intentionally focusing your attention and energy towards a specific outcome. The more aligned you are with the universe, the easier it becomes to manifest your desires.

In addition to manifestation, prayer and spiritual healing also play a significant role in our lives. Prayer is a form of communication with a higher power, while spiritual healing involves accessing the universal energy to heal and balance the mind, body, and soul.

This chapter briefly overviews energy, vibration, manifestation, prayer, and spiritual healing. However, if this topic does not interest you, you can choose what resonates with you and leave the rest.

Vibrational Frequencies.

Vibrational frequency is a concept that suggests that everything in the universe is energy and each form of energy has a unique frequency. This includes physical objects but it also includes our thoughts and emotions. The study of the law of attraction suggests that emotions that feel expansive, peaceful, or exciting have a high vibration. Emotions that feel depressive, envious, or contracted have a lower vibration meaning that our thoughts and emotions can influence the energy we attract into our lives.

If you're consistently emitting positive energy through thoughts of gratitude, joy, and optimism, you are more likely to attract positive experiences and opportunities into your life.

On the other hand, if you focus on negative thoughts or emotions, you may attract experiences that align with those lower frequencies.

Our Emotions.

When I first learned about this subject, I was terrified to think of any negative thoughts. This became exhausting and even debilitating at times. An easier, more straightforward way to grasp your thoughts is to look at your general emotions. Our emotions are like an internal guidance system that helps us understand whether we are on the right track or need to shift our focus. Positive emotions indicate that we align with our desires while negative emotions signal a misalignment. Gratitude is a powerful tool to change your emotional state and can become a powerful tool in your arsenal to attract your desires to you.

Intentions.

At the beginning of Part Two of this book, we spoke about becoming crystal clear about our goals and intentions because clarity on our goals directs our energy towards manifesting desirable outcomes. Visualization and affirmations are standard practices associated with this process, aiding you to align your thoughts and feelings with your desired reality. When you visualize your desired outcomes and shift your identity around your ability to achieve those goals, you create a powerful energy that helps manifest those intentions into reality.

We Are Energy.

It is all energy! What's beautiful about this is knowing that we and all other things are connected through universal laws. We can influence the world around us through our vibration. We can either repel or attract people, experiences, and circumstances. That's a fantastic amount of power!

Energy is constantly moving in and out of form. It is never stagnant or permanent. This is good news! It means that your circumstances can be changed by changing the energy that your mind is in. Increase your frequency and the frequency of your life changes.

You may think how do we change our frequency?? By changing our thoughts and actions, choosing gratitude in times of suffering, telling ourselves a different story, and changing our habits to lift us rather than drain us. It's everything we have been discussing in this entire book!

You may have noticed that your frequency has already begun to change and some of your circumstances have already started to rearrange and shift with this change. As a result, you are manifesting positive change in your life.

Now, the trick is not to control the steps to that change. Sometimes the transition is smooth and easy; other times, the transition comes into your life to break down old patterns of generational traumas or to break up dense, stuck energy. This is where we often go wrong; we dislike the discomfort that comes with the breakdown before the change and so we try to push it away. However, this isn't a judgment of "good" or "bad. " Everything is, and it has the opportunity to serve you if you let it.

There is only the journey, which sometimes feels light and easy and sometimes heavy and complex, yet your dreams are still coming into form. It is up to you to trust the process. Instead, get curious in those difficult times and ask yourself what your dream needs from you rather than what you need from it!

Spiritual Healing After Adversity.

Adversity is a challenging experience that can deeply affect our spirituality and beliefs. It can shake us to the core, leaving us feeling lost, confused, and questioning the purpose of our existence. We want to comprehend why these things happened to us. Searching for meaning is normal and natural. However, clarity will come when you get curious rather than powerless about the world around you. Meditation, prayer, or mindfulness facilitate this connection, nurturing a sense of peace and serenity, even in tumultuous times.

Through introspection and reflection, we can connect with our inner selves, our beliefs, values, and higher purpose. This process often leads to a deeper understanding of ourselves and the world around us, allowing us to emerge from our struggles stronger and more profound than before.

Despite the benefits of this journey, it's important to note that it's a choice we have to make. We must actively choose to engage in this process of growth and transformation rather than allowing our struggles to consume us. It takes courage, determination, and willingness to face our fears and vulnerabilities. But the rewards of this journey are immeasurable, offering us the opportunity to become the best version of ourselves.

Seeking Meaning.

For myself, I have come to the inner knowing that my cancer was a blessing in disguise. It brought me closer to myself. Something I had asked God/Universe for. I can still remember the prayer I spoke. I asked God to guide me to my purpose and my calling and to set me free from the shackles of my people-pleasing, low self-worth, low self-esteem, tumultuous relationships, disharmony in my work life, and constant fear that I wasn't good enough. I remember crying in my car and telling God I was ready for "whatever is in store for me if I can set myself free from myself." Within eight months of my prayer, I was diagnosed with cancer.

As crazy as it sounds, the meaning I have assigned to my cancer is that it was an answered prayer. I believe this to be true because all the things I asked for came true because of my journey. Sure, I would have preferred the journey to be easier but I suspect I would not have learned as much if the journey had been easy. This has given me a great deal of peace.

Prayer and Belief.

Faith was a huge component in my healing. Having something to believe in, pray to, and draw strength from was pivotal in my journey. Without a greater purpose and a belief that my journey was here for a reason, I would not have been able to get through with the grace and strength that I exhibited.

"God" does not need to be your term. I know I used to be much more comfortable with the word "universe." It seemed less strict and more open. However, over time, facing the Grim Reaper, I began to shed the layers I had around the word "God." I began to see that my body was a miracle and was of God. Therefore, miraculous healing could occur because I was a miracle, so miracles were innate. This process began to break down my walls around the word "God. " I am not religious in the conventional sense, but my beliefs have deepened beautifully.

How can you access a belief that fills your soul with hope in times of challenge? What term can you get comfortable with? Where can you put your worries and fears when all hope seems lost? Surrendering to something beyond ourselves can bring us a great deal of peace in times of struggle.

Everything is Cyclical.

The world we live in is characterized by cycles. These cycles are evident in the changing of the seasons, the rotation of planets, and the menstrual cycles in mammals. Life itself is a cycle that encompasses good and bad times, challenges and successes, even life and death.

It's important to understand that similar to how the earth orbits a star and the ocean tides follow the moon, life also has its natural cycles. When you find yourself in a difficult season of life, it's essential to remember that this, too, shall pass.

Recognizing that these cycles are not limited to the natural world is important. They also exist in our personal lives, relationships, and work. When we encounter difficult times, it's natural to feel overwhelmed and believe the situation will never improve. However, it's crucial to remember that everything in life is cyclical, and with time, the problem is bound to change for the better.

Manifestation.

This is the process in which you are attracting and drawing things toward you. It is commonly known as "The Law of Attraction." However, many other laws govern the universe. Some people believe that there are twelve, eighteen, or even hundreds of these laws. The important thing to understand and keep in mind is that manifestation is more holistic than what people usually think.

When most people hear the term "manifestation," they think about attracting wealth, health, love, and abundance. However, manifestation is happening all the time, even when you are not aware of it. Everything that you know and understand about your reality has been manifested by you through your experiences, thoughts, and understanding of the world.

You may find it difficult to hear that you have manifested undesirable situations such as debt, failed relationships, or poor health. However, the good news is that you have the power to change this. You can manifest the opposite of those things and start a new path. Both the life you are living and the life you want are possible. It is up to you to choose which one you want to manifest.

Manifesting Illness.

I don't have all of the answers, but one thing that I don't agree with or appreciate is the notion that you "manifested your disease because you didn't deal with your emotional baggage." I believe this can be true for some; years and years of neglecting our emotional needs can create trapped energy in the body which, over time, can lead to illness. However, there are nuances to that statement. I believe illness is a wake-up call for some to come into their souls purpose in life; for others, it is a lesson learned; for others, perhaps a soul contract to exit this life, etc. The point I'm trying to make is that nothing in this world is concrete. Every person is unique, and every experience is exceptional. Blaming the survivor with this blanket statement is a black-and-white thought process. This statement blames the survivor for not doing their due diligence. That doesn't help anyone.

Instead, I invite you to consider that like the world around us, it is much more complex than that. Illness shows up in our lives for many different reasons and heals for many other reasons (lifestyle, stress, generational trauma, trapped energy, grief, physical activity, genetics, etc.).

Let us take a curious approach. What seems correct for you regarding disease, challenge, or adversity? Why do you think "bad" things happen to you? What feels like a truth and what feels not as applicable? We all have intuition and if we can strengthen our commitment and believe in our intuition, the answers can become apparent.

Throughout my journey, I know that many people told me what to do, when to do it, why I got sick, and what I needed to do to become well. However, after a while, I stopped listening and asked myself what was true. As time went on, my conviction became stronger and stronger. I healed miraculously and I continue to remain cancer-free. And I didn't listen to a lot of credible people. That, to me, is proof that my intuition is paramount enough regarding health and healing. I believe yours is, too.

I invite you to strengthen your resolve in your intuition and begin to listen to that little voice inside. It will set you free.

☑ **Action Step**: Book yourself in for some energy work. Have you been craving a meditation session, gong bath, breathwork, retreat or other? Give energy work a try and see how it feels.

📖 **Journal Questions**:

1. Reflect on the concept of manifestation and the law of attraction. How do your thoughts, beliefs, and intentions shape the energy you attract into your life? Write about any experiences you've had with consciously manifesting your desires or goals.

EIGHTEEN

Integrate

INTEGRATE WHAT YOU HAVE LEARNED

Congratulations on making it through! You have done beautifully, and your changes so far are creating the most beautiful evolution of yourself. With time, understanding, patience, radical responsibility, and integrity, you will continue to see the fruits of your labour here. Now, I know you are wondering how to obtain and keep your positive changes... Read on!

Integration:

As you step into this next chapter of your life, I want you to bring with you these crucial practices.

- **Be integral and radically responsible:** A.K.A stop living where life is "to you" and instead come from a place where life is "for you." What do I need right now to weather this season of my life? Then, ask: What can I learn from this experience? Now, spring into action and do what you must to set yourself up for success.
- **Set aside time for intentional rest:** Schedule it into your day, tell your family, and pay for it if you have to. Set aside time for intentional rest. Understand that this

is by far the most crucial tool in your toolbox. We are not meant to push our entire lives. Save time in your busy schedule by setting aside a tiny period for yourself daily with some type of intentional rest.

- **Be aware of your "stories":** Watch out for your melodrama and your own stories telling you you can't have everything you want. Complaining leads to more things to complain about. Remember that!
- **Never compromise who you are for anyone:** Always be authentic. Even if you are scared, it will polarize others. That's a them problem; dimming your light for other people's comfort is A) hurting you and B) not allowing others to live their truth.
- **Always be in abundance:** Find gratitude for everything you have and everything that is coming. Believe on a deep level that you can and do have everything you need and more. This life is full of potential for you. Get clear on what you want and go after it. Feel the fear and do it anyway! If you miss the mark, it is only because you didn't believe you could have it.
- **Understand that discomfort is part of life:** Discomfort is a sign of growth. Allow discomfort to be part of your life and stop trying to push it away. This is what makes life… life. The ebb and flow. The yin and yang. The night and day. Allow all seasons and all things to be okay whether it is outside of your comfort zone or not.

You Have Changed.

There are no two ways about it. Your experiences, challenges, and adversities have completely changed you, which can be good. It is time to embrace this version of you that has laid dormant for years. The version of you that has always existed but has been hidden under all sorts of programs and limiting beliefs is ready to emerge!

Who do you want to be after learning this knowledge? How do you want to conduct yourself in the world? What experiences, pleasures, journeys, and lessons do you want in your life? The choice is yours.

Integration and Your Health.

Throughout these chapters, we have invested a significant amount of time and effort into discussing your health. Now, it's time for you to take control and determine what balance means to you. Everyone has their unique version of balance and your definition may differ from others. It is essential to tap into your intuition and identify what you need to do to maintain good health.

As you embark on this journey, consider what brings you joy, what makes you feel alive, and what excites you. Taking care of your health requires time and effort but it should also be inspiring and fulfilling. If you don't feel motivated, don't be afraid to explore different options until you find what works best for you. There is no time frame for change.

Remember, good health is not a one-size-fits-all solution and it's okay to experiment until you find the right balance. What's important is that you prioritize your health and make choices that will help you feel your best. Take some time to reflect and figure out what you need to do to maintain a healthy and balanced life.

Integration and Relationships.

What have you discovered about yourself while reading this book? How has this newfound self-awareness affected your relationships? Do you feel a disconnect between how you want to be treated and how you are currently being treated? Are you concerned that your personal growth may lead to outgrowing your partner or friends?

These are common questions that arise when we undergo significant individual changes in our lives. It is essential to recognize that personal growth takes time and it may also take your loved ones some time to adjust to the new you.

Your current life is a reflection of your subconscious beliefs and values. It is important to remain patient and true to yourself while you work towards becoming the best version of you. Always remember, it is never too late to make positive changes in your life and relationships, as long as both parties are committed to putting in the effort.

As you explore yourself and life, you will discover the true value of your relationships. You will find that the people who truly matter in your life will mirror your changes after a brief period of adjustment, while those who don't will naturally fall away.

Your primary responsibility is to take care of yourself and prioritize your needs. By taking care of yourself you will be able to show up for others from a place of abundance rather than depletion or resentment. Remember, you cannot pour from an empty cup. Taking care of yourself is not selfish; it is necessary for your well-being and the well-being of those around you.

Integration and Your Work.

The workplace can often be a challenging environment to be in, especially when you are trying to create your dream life. Perhaps you feel like your boss or superiors are forcing you to do things that you don't want to do. Alternatively, you may have ideas on changing your work environment but your superiors will not allow you creative liberty. Creating a positive work environment starts with respecting yourself and your needs.

Achieving a newfound respect may require a significant shift in your career or establishing better boundaries within your current career. You know what's best for you and your family.

It's important to remember that your life is a reflection of what you believe you deserve. So, what is your work life like? This can be a clue to your overall satisfaction with the way things are going in your life. The old adage, "Life is hard and then you die," is becoming outdated and the newer generations can see through these illusions. While life can undoubtedly be challenging, it should not be overly complicated. We complicate our own lives with our choices, actions, and thoughts.

So, how can we change your work situation? Here's a hint... the first thing that needs to change is your mindset. I remember being in jobs that I despised and when people talked about mindset, my initial reaction was always, "It's easy for you to say your boss isn't an idiot." In that example, I was making excuses for myself and not taking responsibility for my actions and reactions in my own life. I didn't believe that I had any control and was afraid to make mistakes so I attributed everything to my boss. Blaming others is not essential or radically responsible.

It's important to realize that you always have a choice. You can choose to change your work situation through boundary-setting and self-preservation or you can choose to quit. It's okay to make a change if you're unhappy or unfulfilled in your current position. Ultimately, taking responsibility for your own life and career is the key to creating a positive work environment.

Integration and Money.

Money can be viewed as a form of energy exchange. It's a give-and-take process where you offer your energy in exchange for something else. If you're not fully satisfied with the energy you're putting in or what you're receiving in return, it may create disharmony and dissatisfaction.

Note: When I say "energy exchange," I do not mean effort exchange. If effort were the key, then every house cleaner, carpenter, teacher, etc. would be rich. No, money is an energy exchange which means a frequency exchange. The higher your frequency, the closer money draws to you. When you feel joy, peace, abundance, gratitude, etc., you are in a place of creativity; this creativity sparks ideas that lead to more money. Alternatively, when you are worn down, fearful, in scarcity, and unhappy, your imagination is low; therefore, ideas to attract more income will not come.

For example, if you're at a job you hate, it can affect your energy levels, ultimately leading to an unsatisfactory energy exchange. As a result, it's unlikely that you'll experience an abundance of money.

However, it's not as simple as being happy all the time to attract more money. Instead, it's about recognizing that there are no limits to your earning potential. The only limits are those that you impose on yourself due to your beliefs, stories, and projections.

To achieve a positive exchange of energy and abundance in money, choose to be willing to put in the effort. This means examining your subconscious thoughts, beliefs, and projections and being open to change. It may also require stepping out of your comfort zone and taking risks.

But the reward for making these changes can be life-altering. You'll be able to achieve the life you've always dreamed of, with the financial freedom and abundance to pursue your passions and live your best life.

It's Time to Live Life More Intentionally.

So, by now, you can see that we are 100% responsible for the things we get to enjoy or not enjoy in this life. As of now, we can see that life is our responsibility. It is time to pick up your pen and rewrite your stories. It is time for you to harness your innate internal power. Now it is time for you to accept you are pure potential.

When you do this, know that it is going to be uncomfortable! However, on the other side of this discomfort is the life you have always dreamt of living. It's time to reassess what you truly want. Now, after all of this self-growth and change. it is time for you to evolve.

Embracing Transformation.

In this journey of self-discovery and empowerment, we've navigated the intricacies of change, resilience, and growth. Each chapter has been a stepping stone toward unlocking the immense potential within.

Throughout these pages, we've explored the profound resilience of the human spirit in the face of adversity. We've uncovered the power of mindset shifts, the importance of self-compassion, and the transformative force of gratitude, spirituality, and holistic healing practices.

But this journey doesn't end here; it's a continuum—a lifelong journey of self-discovery and empowerment. The lessons learned, the tools acquired, and the perspectives gained will inevitably illuminate the path ahead.

Change isn't a singular event—it's a series of choices, actions, and beliefs. These choices will bring you the results you want or don't want. It's about embracing discomfort, finding strength in vulnerability, and fostering resilience in facing challenges.

As you close this book, choose to continue learning these lessons, allow the momentum to catch up, and allow these lessons to change your life as they did mine. Let every obstacle become a stepping stone, every setback a lesson, and every moment an opportunity for growth.

Believe in the power within you to shape your reality, redefine your limits, and craft a life of purpose, resilience, and unwavering authenticity.

So, take a step forward with courage. Embrace transformation. Embody resilience. And may your journey be a testament to the boundless potential in your heart and soul.

It is not the end; it's the beginning of a remarkable journey toward self-mastery, fulfillment, and a life of unbounded passion and purpose.

Thank you for reading,

Christine

Change takes time, accountability, and support. Should you choose *you* and your evolution, I will be waiting for you. I am here to be your guide, integrate the above material, and dive even deeper into your evolution. Don't let this book and these transformations fall away. Join me in one of my signature programs and let's evolve together.

Enjoy A Free Meditation

Snag Your Complimentary Meditation Session

....

With this book, you'll receive a complimentary meditation designed to assist you in transforming challenges into resilience. This exclusive meditation is specifically for readers of this book. Just scan the QR code provided below to access it.

Free Meditation

This is a meditation that offers support in transforming pain into strength. Embrace the role of the alchemist in your own journey. Use this meditation alongside the book "Unbroken: Rising Above, Thriving Within" for an enhanced experience. Enjoy!

Interested In Learning More About Live Free Wellness?

If you are interested in learning about Live Free Wellness education, 1:1 sessions, public speaking, or free supports, scan the code here to select your preferences. I will reach out via email with the information you requested.

Your Health Is Your Wealth

Thank You For Reading

· ·

Mentioned throughout the book is both Breast cancer and Lung cancer. Two health concerns that require your attention. To learn more about what you can do to protect your health refer to the resources below.

Self Breast Check

Checking your breasts monthly for changes is an effective prevention measure that can aid in avoiding late stage diagnosis. Early stage cancer is more curative than late stage and therefor a regular regime is effective and recommended. Please see the QR code for more information.

Home Radon Gas Check

Radon gas is a colourless, odourless gas that comes from the breakdown in uranium in the soil. This gas can come into your home through small openings and is a known carcinogen. My childhood home had high levels of radon gas and without the knowledge of this gas we did not remove it. As a result my lung cancer was suspected to have been a result of this gas. To learn more and how to test your home scan the QR code.

About the Author

Born and raised in rural Saskatchewan to a loving family. I have always had a genuine desire to help people and make a difference in the world. In 2020, I was handed a devastating late stage cancer diagnosis that abruptly shifted my focus to a whirlwind of diagnostic measures, appointments and life changing treatments to simply, stay alive.

Now in remission, I choose to share my lessons with people from all walks of life in the hopes that they too can turn their pain into their power. I am committed to providing individuals who have faced adversity with the necessary tools, inspiration, and hope to transform their pain into resilience. My primary objective is to assist people in overcoming challenges by utilizing those situations to become more powerful and purposeful than ever before.

One thing in life is constant, and that is change. How can we use our experiences to evolve?

Connect with me by scanning the QR code. Here you will find links to my Podcast, education, 1:1 mentorship, programs and courses, socials and so much more.

Manufactured by Amazon.ca
Acheson, AB

13055855R00116